VOLUME 1

FUNK & WAGNALLS WILDLIFE ENCYCLOPEDIA

GENERAL EDITORS • Dr. Maurice Burton and Robert Burton

Also published as The International Wildlife Encyclopedia and Encyclopedia of Animal Life.
Funk & Wagnalls, Inc., New York, New York

Preface

During the past 30 years of Funk & Wagnalls' almost 100 years of existence, we have become the leader in bringing reference works to the public at realistic prices. This sales technique is operated principally through supermarket outlets and in the main, products brought to the public have been Funk & Wagnalls encyclopedias and closely related products.

In the course of our history. Funk & Wagnalls has gained a close insight into both the reference needs and the household budget of the average family. We have learned what types of books they want and the price ranges they will tolerate.

We found that in the average family's reference requirements, there seems to be an interest in, and need for a reference work specifically dedicated to the animals, birds, fish, insects and reptiles of the world.

Interest in our fellow creatures has, no doubt, been heightened recently by our concerns about ecology and endangered species. The photos taken of our planet from space by the astronauts dramatically demonstrated to us that we were living on this lonesome sphere together with other creatures, and we realized that each of their species is unique and irreplaceable.

We set about to search for such a reference product hoping that one existed, for we knew that if it did not, we would create one ourselves.

(continued)

Preface *(continued)*

Happily, we found a reference work which satisfied our demand for beauty and quality in illustration and reliability of authorship. The work was originally published in the United Kingdom and is now printed in several languages and sold in many countries throughout the world. This Funk & Wagnalls Wildlife Encyclopedia is also offered to the public as the International Wildlife Encyclopedia, sold as a 20 volume set through direct mail and as the Encyclopedia of Animal Life, sold in 96 parts in magazine form through newsstands.

As mentioned above, we have gained insight into not only what the public wants, but what it can afford and will spend for reference works. Based on this knowledge and our expertise in high volume reference book production we have been able to bring this work to you at about half the price at which it has previously been offered, with a concurrent need for reduction of content by only two percent.

We are proud to bring you Funk & Wagnalls Wildlife Encyclopedia and hope you will be able to collect the full 22 volumes at this low price and in this convenient manner.

We also hope that you and your family will enjoy the set for many years to come.

F. J. Scully, *President*
Funk & Wagnalls, Inc.
Publishers, New York, N.Y.

Aardvark

African mammal with a bulky body, 6 ft long including a 2 ft tail, and standing 2 ft high at the shoulder. Its tough grey skin is so sparsely covered with hair that it often appears naked except for areas on the legs and hind quarters. The head is long and narrow, the ears donkey-like; the snout bears a round pig-like muzzle and a small mouth. The tail tapers from a broad root. The feet have very strong claws— four on the front feet and five on the hind feet. The name is the Afrikaans for 'earth-pig'.

△ *Aardvark at home in African scrub close to a termites' nest where it has been feeding on these soft-bodied insects.*

▽ *The aardvark's nose is guarded by a fringe of bristles and it can also close its nostrils, as a protection against termites.*

Distribution and habits

The aardvark has powerful limbs and sharp claws so it can burrow into earth at high speed. This it does if disturbed away from its accustomed burrow. There are records of it digging faster than a team of men with spades. When digging, an aardvark rests on its hind legs and tail and pushes the soil back under its body with its powerful fore feet, dispersing it with the hind legs.

The normal burrow, usually occupied by a lone aardvark, is 3–4 yd long, with a sleeping chamber at the end, big enough to allow the animal to turn round. Each animal has several burrows, some of them miles apart. Abandoned ones may be taken over by warthogs and other creatures.

Years can be spent in Africa without seeing an aardvark, although it is found throughout Africa south of the Sahara, except in dense forest. Little is known of its habits as it is nocturnal and secretive, though it may go long distances for food, unlike other burrowing animals.

Termite feeder

The aardvark's principal food is termites. With its powerful claws it can rip through the wall of termite nests that are difficult for a man to break down even with a pick.

Its method is to tear a small hole in the wall with its claws; at this disturbance the termites swarm, and the aardvark then inserts its slender 18 in. tongue into the hole and picks the insects out. It is protected from their attacks by very tough skin and the ability to close its nostrils—which are further guarded by a palisade of stiff bristles.

As well as tearing open nests, the aardvark will seek out termites in rotten wood or while they are on the march. It also eats other soft-bodied insects and some fruit, but—unlike the somewhat similar pangolin, which has a muscular, gizzard-like stomach filled with grit for crushing hard-bodied insects—it cannot deal with true ants.

Breeding cycle

The single young (twins happen occasionally) is born in midsummer in its mother's burrow, emerging after two weeks to accompany her on feeding trips. For the next few months it moves with her from burrow to burrow, and at six months is able to dig its own.

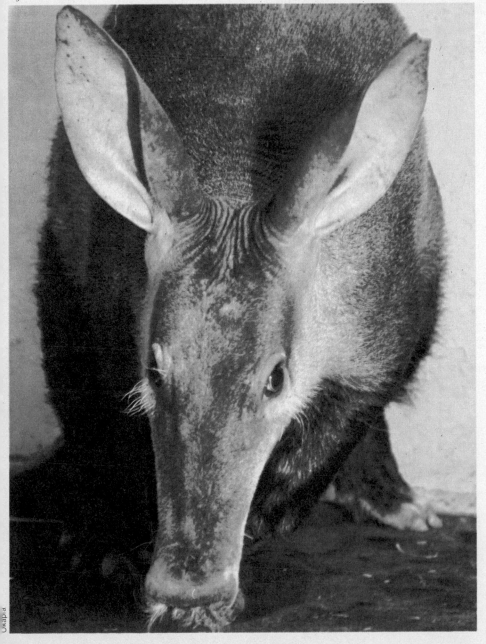

Okapia

Popperfoto

Popperfoto

Digs to escape enemies

The aardvark's main enemies are man, hunting dogs, pythons, lions, cheetahs and leopards, and also the honey badger or ratel, while warthogs will eat the young. When suspicious it sits up kangaroo-like on its hind quarters, supported by its tail, the better to detect danger. If the danger is imminent it runs to its burrow or digs a new one; if cornered, it fights back by striking with the tail or feet, even rolling on its back to strike with all four feet together. On one occasion, when an aardvark had been killed by a lion, the ground was torn up in all directions, suggesting that the termite-eater had given the carnivore a tough struggle for its meal. However, flight and—above all—superb digging ability are the aardvark's first lines of defence for, as with other animals with acute senses like moles and shrews, even a moderate blow on the head is fatal.

A creature on its own

One of the most remarkable things about the aardvark is the difficulty zoologists have had in finding it a place in the scientific classification of animals. At first it was placed in the order Edentata (the toothless ones) along with the armadillos and sloths, simply because of its lack of front teeth (incisors and canines). Now it is placed by itself in the order Tubulidentata (the tube-toothed) so called because of the fine tubes radiating through each tooth. These teeth are in themselves very remarkable, for they have no roots or enamel.

So the aardvark is out on an evolutionary limb, a species all on its own with no close living relatives. Or perhaps we should say rather that it is on an evolutionary dead stump, the last of its line.

What is more, although fossil aardvarks have been found—but very few of them—in North America, Asia, Europe and Africa, they give us no real clue to the aardvark's ancestry or its connections with other animals.

class	**Mammalia**
order	**Tubulidentata** *sole representative*
family	**Orycteropidae**
genus	
& species	***Orycteropus afer***

◁ *The wall of a termite nest is so hard it is difficult for a man to break down even with a pick-axe but the powerful claws of the aardvark can rip through it easily.*

The termites are so disturbed by having their nest opened that they swarm about and the aardvark then puts its pig-like muzzle into the nest to eat them.

It has an 18 in. long, slender, sticky tongue with which it captures and eats the swarming termites that make up the main food of aardvarks.

▷ *A day-old aardvark. It depends on its mother for six months until it can dig its own burrow. The aardvark's snout and round, pig-like muzzle earn it the Afrikaans name for 'earth-pig'.*

Aardvark escape route

Disturbed away from its burrow, the aardvark can escape its enemies by digging at incredible speed. It forces the soil back with its fore feet and kicks it away with its strong hind legs, 'so fast that it can outstrip a team of six men with spades'.

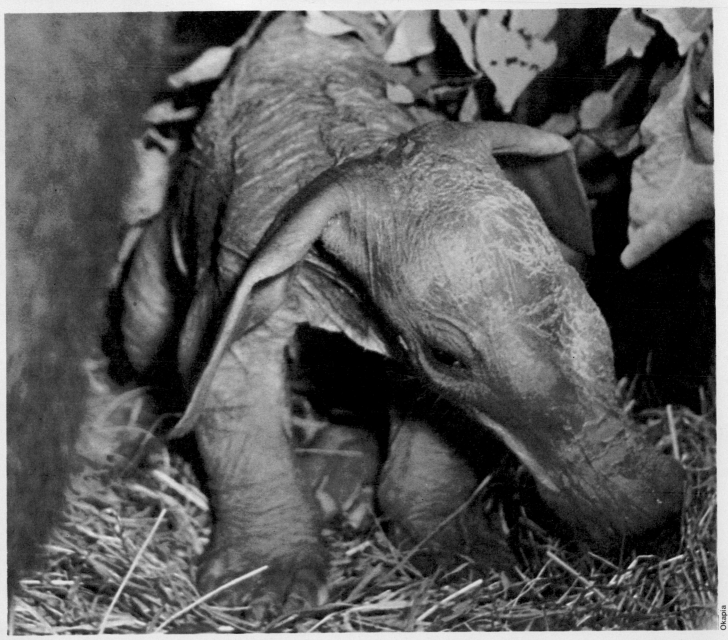

Okapia

Aardwolf in its rock crevice lair. It spends the day here and comes out at night to feed.

Aardwolf

African member of the hyaena family, differing from the true hyaenas in having five instead of four toes on the front feet, relatively larger ears, and a narrower muzzle. Also, the jaws and teeth are weaker than those of the true hyaenas.

The body, somewhat larger than that of a fox, weighs 50–60 lb. The coat is yellow-grey with black stripes, except for the legs, which are black below the knee. The muzzle is black and hairless, the tail bushy and black-tipped. The hair along the back and neck is long: this ridge of hair usually lies flat, but when the animal is frightened it erects the hair around the neck—or, in extreme cases, along the whole back.
The name is Afrikaans for 'earth-wolf'.

Distribution and habits
The aardwolf ranges throughout southern and eastern Africa as far north as Somalia. It is nowhere common but is found most frequently in sandy plains or bushy country.

It is rarely seen, since it is a nocturnal animal and spends the day lying up in rock crevices or in burrows excavated in the soil. The burrow consists of two or more sharply winding tunnels 25–30 ft long, leading to a sleeping chamber about 3 ft in diameter. Abandoned holes of aardvarks are sometimes used.

Little is known about aardwolves' habits. They are usually solitary, but groups of several females with young have been reported as sharing the same burrow.

Termite feeding hyaena
The aardwolf lives almost entirely on termites and other insects, but lacks claws strong enough to tear open termite nests,

so it is limited either to picking up the insects from the surface of the ground, or digging them out of soft soil. The speed and efficiency with which the long tacky tongue sweeps up insects was impressively shown when the stomach of an aardwolf that had been run over was opened up. It contained some 40,000 termites, although the aardwolf was unlikely to have been foraging for more than three hours. This gives an average consumption of at least three termites per second.

When insects are in short supply, the aardwolf may turn to other prey; mice, small birds and eggs of ground-nesting birds are the main victims. Eating carrion has been reported, but it is more likely that the aardwolves were feeding on the beetles and maggots within the carcasses. Accusations of killing lambs and chickens may be true in the case of very hungry individuals, but normally aardwolves in captivity refuse even finely chopped meat. This is probably due to their inadequate dentition; there are few cheek teeth, for chewing, and those are very small. Thus, although they may be able to kill a lamb with their dog-like canine teeth, chewing would present a problem.

Breeding cycle
A single litter of two to four is born each year, in the southern part of the range in November-December. The gestation period ranges from 90 to 110 days. The young are born blind.

Mistaken persecution
The aardwolf's main enemy is man, who tends to kill them in mistake for hyaenas, for which bounty is paid in many areas. Despite their rigid protection by the London Convention for the Protection of Fauna in 1933, the aardwolves have suffered persecution in farming country, both through mistaken identity and the idea that they take poultry.

The natural enemies of the aardwolf are

probably the same as those of the aardvark —pythons, lions and leopards.

For defence, aardwolves can put up a good fight with their long canine teeth and can eject an obnoxious, musky fluid from their anal glands.

Insect-eating carnivores
Aardwolves resemble hyaenas sufficiently for them to be shot by mistake, yet at one time they were classed as a separate family, the Protelidae. Now they are considered to be members of the Hyaenidae but forming a separate genus, *Proteles*.

The reason for the separation from the true hyaenas is their insectivorous habits. For although they have fewer adaptions for feeding on termites than aardvarks—weak claws and no palisade of bristles guarding eyes and nostrils—the aardwolves still show considerable differences from their carnivorous relatives. The hyaenas are hunters and carrion eaters, with powerful neck and jaw muscles and strong teeth. The aardwolf's teeth, by contrast, are a sorry sight. Apart from the fairly large canines, they are ridiculously small, and the cheek teeth are few in number. An aardwolf's skull gives the impression of an animal having died of old age and worn-down teeth.

Aardwolves may have evolved in two possible ways. Either they once had but have now lost the carnivorous features of the hyaenas, or else they diverged from the main hyaena stock before the latter developed their strong teeth and jaws.

class	**Mammalia**
order	**Carnivora**
family	**Hyaenidae**
genus & species	***Proteles cristatus***

Abalone

A genus of single-shelled molluscs related to the limpets. Also known as ormer, sea ear, or earshell, the abalone (four syllables, the final e being sounded) somewhat resembles a snail, the body being little more than a muscular foot with a head at one end, bearing a pair of eyes and sensory tentacles. The body is also fringed with tentacles.

Over the top of the shell lies a line of holes, through which water is exhaled after it has been drawn in under the shell and over the gills to extract oxygen. New holes are formed as the shell grows forward, while the old holes become covered over, so that only a few younger holes are open at any one time, the rest appearing as a line of bumps.

Some abalones are among the largest shellfish: they range in size from the 1 in. long and very rare Haliotis pourtalese to the red abalone of California, which is a foot across.

Helmut Stellrecht

Jane Burton

D.P.Wilson

△ *Abalone showing edge of foot and its frill of tentacles which seek out its seaweed food.*

◁◁ *Mother of pearl, used in making jewellery, lines the inside of the abalone shells.*

◁ *A black abalone without the encrusting seaweeds which grow on most other species.*

▽ *The starfish is one of the abalone's main enemies. It uses its hundreds of sucker feet to prise the abalone away from its rock. The starfish then turns its stomach inside out and pushes it beneath the abalone's shell to dissolve away its flesh.*

Helmut Stellrecht

Distribution, habitat and habits

Abalones are to be found in many parts of the world: along the coasts of the Mediterranean, Africa, Australia, New Zealand, the Pacific islands, and the western coast of North America. In the Atlantic they are found as far north as St. Malo and the Channel Islands. The rare species *Haliotis pourtalese* is found off Florida. It is known mainly from specimens washed up on the shore, as it lives at depths of 350−1,200 ft. It is thus the deepest-living of all abalones; the rest live between the extreme low-water mark and a depth of about 60 ft along rocky shores where there is no sand to clog the gills or in rocky pools large enough not to be heated too quickly by the sun. The only other exception is the black abalone, which lives in the splash zone where waves breaking against rocks alternately cover and expose it.

Unlike their limpet relatives, abalones have no 'home', no spot on a rock where they always return after feeding. They simply hide up in a crevice or under a rock, avoiding the light and coming out at night. When disturbed an abalone grips the rock face, using its foot as a suction pad: the two main muscles of the body exert a tremendous force−up to 400 lb in a 4 in. specimen. Unlike the limpet, the abalone cannot bring its shell down over the whole of its body: the edge of the foot, with its frill of tentacles, is left sticking out.

Abalones move in the same way as limpets and snails. Waves of muscular contraction pass along the foot, pushing it forward. As each part expands it is fixed to the ground by slimy mucus: the part in front, expanding in turn, is pressed forward and then itself stuck down. Abalones differ from limpets and snails in having a sort of bipedal movement. Alternate waves of movement pass down either side of the foot, so that as a part of one side is moving the corresponding part on the other side stays fixed.

The rate of travel is very rapid for a shellfish: a speed of 5−6 yd/min has been recorded−although no abalone would cover this distance in one dash.

7

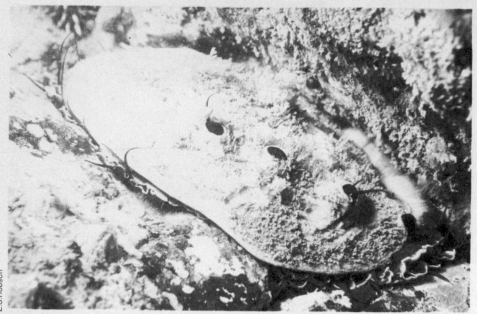

E.S.Hobson

△ *The abalone breathes through the line of holes in the top of its shell. As it grows, new ones form and others are covered over.*

▽ *The remarkable teeth of a radula, the mollusc tongue, magnified 1,450 times by using a deep field scanning electron microscope.*

Many-toothed tongue for feeding

Abalones are vegetarians, crawling over rock faces and browsing on seaweeds that they seek out with their sensitive tentacles. Their favourite foods are the delicate red weeds and green sea lettuces, although they also scrape tissue off fragments of kelp that have been torn away by waves. Young abalones eat the forms of life that encrust rocks, such as the coral-like plant *Corallina*.

Food is scraped up and chewed into small pieces by the rasp-like action of the radula, a tongue made up of large numbers of small, chalky teeth.

100,000 eggs laid

Some molluscs are hermaphrodite but all individual abalones are of one sex or the other. They reach sexual maturity at six years. The germ cells, or gametes, are shed directly into the sea, causing great wastage. Thus a female will liberate 100,000 or more eggs, and the sea around a male turns milky over a radius of 3 ft when he sheds his spawn. To reduce wastage, however, the female does not shed eggs until induced by the presence of sperms around her.

The fertilised eggs are covered by a gelatinous coat and float freely in the sea until they hatch a few hours later as minute trochophore larvae. These trochophore larvae are top-shaped and swim around by means of a band of hair-like cilia around the thickest part. Within a day the trochophore develops into a veliger—a miniature version of the adult complete with shell but still with the band of cilia. Two days later it loses the cilia, sinks to the bottom and starts to develop into an adult, a process that takes several weeks.

The free-swimming larvae have advantages in that they are the means by which the otherwise rather sedentary abalones can spread, but they are very vulnerable and are eaten in their millions by plankton-eating fish like anchovies and herrings.

Enemies everywhere

Although mortality is heaviest during the free-swimming stage, adult abalones also have several enemies. Fish, sea birds, sea otters, crabs and starfish dislodge the abalones or chew bits off them. Their only protection lies in their tenacity in clinging to rocks and the protective camouflage of the shell and foot. This camouflage is improved by the seaweeds and sedentary animals that settle on the shell. Also, it has been found that when young abalones feed on red weeds their shells become red.

On the other hand abalones are more vulnerable due to the boring sponge *Choria lobata*, which erodes holes in their shells and so opens them up to other predators. In the Channel Islands as many as 95% of a sample of abalones have been found to be infected with boring sponges.

Dark pearls, called blister pearls, are sometimes found in abalones. Like the real pearls of oysters, these are formed by the animal to cover up a source of irritation—in this case a minute parasitic clam, *Pholadidea parva*, that bores through the abalone's shell and into its tissues.

Prized for shell and meat

The shells of abalones are prized because, although they are superficially rough and dull, cleaning reveals the gleam of mother of pearl. This and the large size of the shell make abalones popular with shell collectors, and they are also used for making costume jewellery. The body itself is much esteemed as food. The large foot is cut into strips, beaten with a mallet to make it soft, and then fried. The edge of the foot is trimmed off to make chowder.

The popularity of abalones and the ease with which they can be collected from the shore has led to stocks being severely depleted. In California, which is the centre of the abalone industry, only strict laws have prevented its extinction. As abalones do not breed until they are six years old and perhaps 4 in. long, there is a minimum length at which they can be taken: for the common red abalone this is 7 in., corresponding to about 12 years of age. There is a close season—though it now seems that abalones breed all the year round—and catches are limited to five a day and can only be taken by a licence-holder.

Finally, abalone meat cannot be exported from the State of California. This does not mean, however, that it cannot be obtained outside California, as tinned abalone meat is exported from Mexico and Japan.

phylum	**Mollusca**
class	**Gasteropoda**
order	**Prosobranchiata**
genera	***Haliotis rufescens*** (red abalone)
	H. fulgens (green abalone)
	H. cracherodii (black abalone)
	others

Accentor

The name of 12 species of small, rather sparrow-like birds forming a single genus and family. They differ from sparrows in having slender and finely pointed bills and a well developed tenth primary wing feather. They are generally regarded as being related to the thrushes or the warblers.

Two accentors are found in Europe. One, the dunnock or hedge sparrow (but not in fact a sparrow at all) is a rather featureless bird, identifiable by the grey on its breast, neck and head and its dark brown wings. Its song, which can be heard virtually all the year round, is a hurried jingle rather reminiscent of that of the wren.

The other European species is the alpine accentor. This is a larger bird, more brightly coloured than the dunnock; it has a whitish bib spotted with black and conspicuous white-bordered chestnut feathers on the sides of the body.

Habits and habitat

Accentors are found throughout Europe and Asia. The dunnock can be seen all over Europe except in parts of the far north and south. In Britain it is common wherever there is suitable habitat except in the north, where it becomes rarer—it is seldom seen in the Shetlands. Of the several subspecies in Britain and the European continent one is confined to the Hebrides and parts of Scotland.

The alpine accentor is found on mountain ranges from Spain to Japan, extending down to North Africa. Occasionally individuals wander into Britain.

The typical habitat of accentors is in mountainous regions, often well above the tree line and up to the snow line. The Himalayan accentor is found breeding as high as 17,000 ft above sea level, and one race of the alpine accentor breeds up to 18,500 ft above sea level. However, most species breed in the scrub vegetation at rather lower levels. Some species are hardy enough to spend the winter at high altitudes, but others migrate downwards. The remainder live in forests. The dunnock is to be found in many kinds of habitats, but especially in gardens, hedgerows, copses and scrubland.

Accentors are quiet and unobtrusive, remaining close to the ground in the undergrowth. If flushed they fly low and in undulating fashion to cover. On the ground they proceed by leisurely hops or a kind of creeping walk, with the body almost horizontal. The wings are often flicked in a characteristic manner—this is most noticeable in the dunnock during courtship and has earned it the name of shuffle-wing.

Most species in the accentor's family, the Prunellidae, tend to live together in flocks. The dunnock, however, is usually a solitary bird, coming together in small groups only for feeding and a peculiar wing-flicking display. There is little migration—it is

Eric Hosking

mainly just from higher to lower ground and from far north to south. Vagrants of the alpine accentor, however, have reached the Faroes, and the Siberian accentor has turned up in Alaska.

Insects in summer, seeds in winter

During the summer months accentors are insectivorous, eating spiders and insects such as beetles, butterflies and flies. In winter they live almost entirely on seeds and berries, even picking them out of animal

In England, the fast-disappearing hawthorn hedge is a favourite nesting site for the dunnock, or hedge-sparrow. The female makes the nest from leaves, twigs, moss and grass. The male plays no part in nest building or incubation.

9

droppings. They have a finch-like crop and muscular gizzard, and swallow grit to help in breaking up the seeds.

Breeding

The males sing from rocks or low bushes, sometimes making short, lark-like song flights. Among dunnocks the male plays no part in building the nest or in incubation. The female makes the nest in a rock crevice or in a shrub, out of leaves, twigs, moss and grasses, sometimes with a few feathers (dunnocks very occasionally use a lot of feathers for the lining). Sometimes an old blackbird's or swallow's nest is used. The nest is cup-shaped, and five dark blue eggs are laid in it. The hen incubates for about 12 days, leaving the nest only to feed. In other species the male shares in nest-building and incubation.

The young are fed by both parents and fledge in about 12 days. Those of the alpine accentor sometimes leave the nest before they can fly. Dunnocks have two and sometimes three broods a year.

Sings in all seasons

In musical parlance an accentor is one who takes the leading part in singing. We should therefore expect birds called accentors to be outstanding either for their song or for some other feature. In fact they are all relatively inconspicuous birds—the name 'dunnock' refers to the dun plumage. They tend to live in inaccessible places and also to make great use of cover.

Perhaps one of the most outstanding features of these birds is that they do no harm to anybody or anything. They feed on insects and other small animals such as spiders, and in their diet they confer only benefits on man in his agriculture and horticulture. There are few birds with such an unblemished record in this respect.

Nor is the song of an accentor particularly loud or distinguished. But it is persistent. The dunnock, for example, has a short, high-pitched song that is heard at all seasons, by night as well as by day. It is most constantly and vigorously repeated when the bird is excited, as when two rival males meet or the birds are courting. The dunnock is evidently a very light sleeper and will respond to the slightest disturbance at night with a snatch of melody: you can hear it sing in the bush as you pass, especially if you shine a torch towards it. It will also respond by singing to a sudden gust of wind or a scud of rain. Although the breeding season is not particularly early in the spring, the dunnock's courtship begins in December and its song gains vehemence at that time when the weather keeps most birds more silent than usual.

John Markham

△ *The red lining in a young dunnock's mouth stimulates the parents to drop food in. Parents will 'feed' imitation mouths if they are red.*

▽*One race of the alpine accentor has been found as high as 18,500 ft above sea level, feeding on insects caught in mountain air currents.*

Richard Vaughan

class	**Aves**
order	**Passeriformes**
family	**Prunellidae**
genus	***Prunella modularis*** *(dunnock)*
& species	***P. collaris*** *(alpine accentor)*
	10 other species

Addax horns, curving out from the base and spiralling over the back, are considered the most graceful of any animal's. They can reach nearly 1 yd in length and are so prized by hunters that the addax is now very rare.

Addax

A single species in the antelope family, closely related to the oryxes. Also known as the screwhorn antelope, it differs from most antelopes in the absence of facial glands and in the large square teeth, which are more like those of cattle.

An adult male standing some 40 in. at the shoulder weighs about 250 lb. The colouring of the coat varies with the season: in winter it is greyish brown with white hind quarters, under-parts and legs; in summer the body becomes sandy or almost white. The head is white and distinctly marked with brown and black patches to form a white X over the nose. Between the horns is a tuft of long black hairs, and there is a short mane on the neck. The tail is short and slender, tipped with a tuft of hair.

Both sexes bear horns, the female's being somewhat thinner. The horns are like those of the oryx but curve out from the base and spiral back over the neck. A length of nearly 1 yd, measured in a straight line from base to tip, with 1½–3 spiral turns, may be attained.

Habitat

At one time the addax extended across North Africa into Arabia and Palestine. The ancient Egyptians kept it in at least semi-domestication: pictures in a tomb dating from 2500 BC show addax and other antelopes wearing collars and tethered to stakes. It seems also that the number of addax a man owned was an indicator of wealth and position. Certainly the addax would have been among the most beautiful of status symbols.

More recently, addax were to be found from Algeria to the Sudan, but never farther south than a line drawn roughly from Dakar to Khartoum. Now they are much restricted and becoming increasingly rare: numbers are estimated at about 5,000. Precise details of captive addax are recorded in a stud book held at San Diego Zoo, USA. During 1966 and 1967, in seven zoos throughout the world, 33 offspring were bred.

There have been two causes of this reduction. First, their habitat is being destroyed by the opening up of desert areas for commercial projects, in addition to the destruction of its sparse vegetation by herds of domestic goats. Secondly, the addax themselves are being killed by hunters. The horns are considered the most graceful of any animal's—a sure cause of persecution—and the hide is used for shoe leather. The addax is slow by comparison with other antelopes,

so it falls an easy prey to man and his dogs. It is not difficult to ride an addax to exhaustion, for it will panic and use up its energy in a blind attempt to maintain a high speed. A mounted hunter following at a gentle trot will exhaust an addax after an hour, and modern hunters in cars can 'blow' one in less than ten minutes. The animal is then so exhausted that it can hardly attempt to defend itself.

In the Sudan, however, the addax's chances of survival are now improving, because the nomads who had been the cause of the reduction in numbers are settling in more hospitable areas away from the addax's haunts. Yet it was only in 1966 that the addax was given formal protection—not that this will be easy to put into practice. One factor meanwhile that enhances its chances of survival is its adaptation to a desert habitat. The hooves are short and widely splayed, enabling it to travel over the sand in the rapid journeys that are a feature of desert animals that have to cover large areas in search of scanty supplies of food.

Moreover, the addax is able to survive in the very depths of the desert where conditions are so extreme that no other warm-blooded animal can survive permanently. Although it can drink large quantities of water at a time, the addax is nevertheless able to survive without any free water almost indefinitely, sufficient water being ob-

tained either from succulent vegetation
or from dew that condenses on plants.

Habits

The addax's habits are not well known,
owing to the thinly spread and inaccessible
nature of the population. Addax are very
wary; at the slightest alarm they dash off at a
frantic gallop. If disturbed too often they
may travel so far as to lose themselves in
the more arid parts of the desert and die of
starvation. In 1963 a camel patrol found
addax spoor and, nearby, a fresh uninjured
carcass of an addax that had apparently
died thus.

Sensitivity to disturbance is increased by
the addax's extreme sensory powers. These
are well developed, as in many desert
animals that live far apart and that would
otherwise have difficulty in locating each
other.

Typically, addax move about in small
troops of 4 – 20 animals – rarely more than
30 – led by an old male. Very occasionally, herds of as many as 300 have been seen.
Normally the troops stay in one area,
providing there is enough vegetation.
Otherwise they may move long distances.

Staple diet of grass

The movements of addax are intimately
related to the distribution of their food,
which in turn is related to the weather.
They are most likely to be found along the
northern fringe of the tropical summer
rains, moving north in winter as the Mediterranean trough system brings rain south-
wards. The addax can tell where the rains
have fallen by scenting from a distance
where the vegetation has turned green.

The staple diet is the *Aristida* grasses,
perennials which may be green throughout
the year, reacting to humid air or rain as
the weather belts pass by. These plants are
sensitive even to a single shower of rain,
sprouting and remaining green all winter.

Addax are fastidious feeders, eating only
certain parts of a plant. When feeding on
the *Aristida* grasses they crop all the blades
to a level height. On the other hand the
outer, dried blades of *Parnicum* grass, the
favoured food of the southern addax, are
not touched. They take only the fresh green
blades, pushing their heads into the middle
of the clump, gripping the growing stems
and breaking them off with an upward jerk
of the head. *Parnicum* seeds are also very
much favoured. They are plucked by drawing the stalk through the mouth so that all
the seeds are cleaned off. As the seeds are
present throughout most of the year and
are rich in protein they form a valuable item
of the addax's diet.

Addax droppings are always covered by a
thin layer of mucus. It has been suggested
that some of the leguminous plants eaten
by the addax secrete viscous fluids which in
turn cause the addax to secrete mucus from
the walls of the intestine. This mucus
layer eases the passage of the rough vegetation and will prevent the dry stalks from
taking up water at the addax's expense.

Breeding unknown

Almost nothing is known about the addax's
breeding except that one young is born at a
time, usually in winter or early spring.

Popperfoto

The shy desert living addax is now very rare because it is ruthlessly hunted, but at the San Diego zoo addax are being bred in captivity.

They beat the censor

During the Second World War, service-
men abroad had their letters censored.
But the urge to let their people at home
know where they were seems to have
been irresistible. Or perhaps it was no more
than a kind of game, to beat the censor. At
all events the methods and means used in
the attempt were numerous, diverse and
ingenious.

The censors were also cunning, and quite
often a letter reached its destination with
little of its contents intact. But one piece of
information was passed by the censor and
succeeded in giving astute families an idea
of where the sender was stationed. American soldiers wrote home describing a 'white
antelope'. Armed with this description
their families went to zoos and got the

animal identified. The white antelope was
the addax – so any reference to a white
antelope indicated the North African
campaign.

class	**Mammalia**
order	**Artiodactyla**
family	**Bovidae**
genus & species	***Addax nasomaculatus***

Adder

A snake, member of the viper family. The adder has a relatively stout body for a snake and a short tail. The average male is 21 in. long, the female 2 ft — the record length is 2 ft 8 in. The head is flat, broadening behind the eyes to form an arrow-head shape.

The colour and body-markings vary considerably; adders are among the few snakes in which male and female are coloured differently. Generally the ground colour is a shade of brown, olive, grey or cream; but black varieties in which all patterning is obliterated are fairly common. The most characteristic marking is the dark zig-zag line down the back with a series of spots on either side; the head carries a pair of dark bands, often forming an X or a V.

It is often possible to distinguish the sex of an adder by its colour. Those which are cream, dirty yellow, silvery or pale grey, or light olive, with black markings, are usually males; females are red, reddish brown or gold, with darker red or brown markings. The throat of the male is black, or whitish with the scales spotted or edged with black; females have a yellowish-white chin sometimes tinged with red.

Distribution and habits

The adder ranges throughout Europe and across Asia to Sakhalin Island, north of Japan. In the British Isles it is absent from Ireland and the northern isles but is the only snake found in Scotland. It is usually to be seen in dry places such as sandy heaths, moors and the sunny slopes of hills where it often basks in the sun on hedge-banks, logs and piles of stones. It is, however, also found in damp situations.

Its tolerance of cold allows the adder to live as far north as Finland, beyond the Arctic Circle. It escapes cold weather by hibernation, which starts when the shade temperature falls below 9°C/49°F. It emerges again when the air temperature rises above 8°C/46°F — even coming out on to snow — but a cold spell will send it in again. The duration of hibernation depends, therefore, on climate: in northern Europe it may last up to 275 days, whereas in the south it may be as little as 105 days. In Britain, adders usually hibernate for about 135 days in October-March, depending on the weather.

Unlike many other snakes adders do not burrow but seek out crevices and holes where they lie up for the winter. The depth at which they hibernate depends, like duration, on the climate: in Britain the average depth is 10–12 in., but in Denmark, where winters are more severe, adders are found at depths of 4 ft.

Very often many adders will be found in one den, or hibernaculum. As many as 40 have been found coiled up together, along with a number of toads and lizards. This massing together is a method of preventing

△ *The adder's tongue looks menacing but is harmless. It is a smell-taste organ, picking up particles from the air and withdrawing them for analysis in the mouth.*

▽ *The hedgehog is one of the adder's arch-enemies. It is protected by its spines while it alternately bites and rolls up, until the adder is dead.*

13

heat loss, but it is not known how the adders come to congregate in the hibernacula, which are used year after year. It may be that they can detect the scent left from previous years.

It is uncertain whether adders are nocturnal or diurnal. Their eyes are typical of nocturnal animals in that they are rich in the very sensitive rod cells: such eyes will see well at night, but during the day they need protection, and the adder's slit pupils cut down the intensity of light. On the other hand, despite these adaptations, adders are often active during the day. Courtship and some feeding are definitely diurnal; the timing of the latter depends on how hungry the adder is.

Rodent killer
The adder's main prey is lizards, mice, voles and shrews. Young adders subsist at first

Geoffrey Kinns AFA

A black adder. Adders range in colour from cream, through dirty yellow to silvery grey or olive (male); and from red to gold (female).

on insects and worms. Larger victims are killed by a poisonous bite, the effects of which vary with the size of the prey. A lizard will be dead within a few minutes, or even within 30 seconds; but an adder's bite is rarely fatal to humans. There were only seven authenticated records of fatalities through snakebite in England and Wales in the first half of this century, and four of these were children.

The adder's method of hunting is to follow its prey by scent, then poison it with a quick strike of the head. While the poison acts, the victim may have time to escape to cover, in which case the snake will wait for a while then follows to eat its dead prey.

Dance of the adders
The mating period is from the end of March to early May, though it has been known to last until autumn. In the north of Europe the summer is too short for the eggs to mature in one year, so breeding takes place in alternate years.

At the beginning of the breeding season, there is a good deal of territorial rivalry between males, culminating in the 'dance of the adders'. Two males face each other with head erect and the forepart of the body held off the ground. They sway from side to side, then with bodies entwined each attempts to force the other to the ground by pushing and thrusting. They do not attempt to bite each other.

Finally one gives up and departs. The female, who is frequently waiting close at hand, will accept any victorious male, if she is ready, and a male will mate with any female. He crawls up behind her and loops his coils over her body, rubbing his chin (which has especially sensitive skin) on her back until he reaches the back of her neck, and mating takes place.

Adders are ovoviviparous: that is, the eggs remain inside the mother's body until they are fully developed, and the young are born coiled up in a membrane which is ruptured by their convulsive movements. They have an egg tooth, which in other animals is used to rupture the egg membranes, but in adders it is degenerate as they have no need of it, and the tooth is so situated that it is of no use for this purpose. It is shed a few days after birth.

The young are born in August or September and the number ranges from five to 20: 10-14 are most common, each measuring 6-8 inches in length. They are immediately capable of independent existence, but often they appear to stay with the mother. Young adders disappear so quickly when disturbed that there is an ancient legend, an account of which appears in Holinshed's Chronicle of 1577, that in times of danger the mother adder swallows her offspring. This legend could be due to early observers cutting up an ovoviviparous mother and finding unborn adders inside. Not knowing that adders hatch from the egg inside the parent they would think she had swallowed them.

Eric Hosking

△ *Male (left) and female adders are always differently coloured.*

▽ *Adder with day-old young.*

Jane Burton: Photo Res.

Stephen Dalton: NHPA

The adder has no external ear or ear drum, but picks up vibrations from the ground through its lower jaw. The vertical slit pupil gives quick perception of horizontal movement.

Enemies although poisonous
Like most animals—even those well capable of defending themselves—adders are most likely to flee if confronted with danger, and they usually bite only if suddenly frightened. But, despite not having the excuse of self-defence, man is their chief enemy. However, the killing of adders on sight has not led to their decline, although nowadays increased urbanisation is destroying their habitat.

Undoubtedly many carnivores will take adders. Foxes and badgers kill them, and they have been found in the stomachs of pike and eels. Surprisingly, perhaps, the hedgehog is a great adversary of adders: one reason is that it can tolerate large doses of venom without harm. Its method of killing is to bite the adder, then curl up leaving nothing but a palisade of spines for the snake to strike at. It repeats the process of biting and curling until the snake is dead, after which the hedgehog eats it.

A confusion of names
The Anglo-Saxon name for the adder was *naedre,* which became 'a nadder' or 'a nedder' in Middle English. Later the *n* was transposed, so that we now have 'an adder'. The alternative name viper comes from the Anglo-Saxon *vipere* or *vipre,* itself derived from the Latin *vipera.* This was a contraction of *vivipara,* from *vivus* (alive) and *parere* (to bring forth)—alluding to the animal's method of reproduction. In general 'viper' was used to mean any venomous snake. There being only one such snake in England, viper and adder became synonymous for the one species (viper also being used to describe a venomous or spiteful person).

The two words have spread with the English language all over the world, being used not only for snakes of the genus *Vipera.* There are the near relatives such as the gaboon viper, more distant, like the pit vipers and mole vipers, and the death adder, which is not even in the viper family.

class	**Reptilia**
order	**Squamata** *suborder Serpentes*
family	**Viperidae**
genus & species	***Vipera berus***

Adélie penguin

Penguins are found in Antarctica, but not the Arctic, and are not, as is often thought, restricted to the frozen land and sea. Various species of penguin live around the coasts of South America, Africa and Australasia, usually not going far north but staying where the sea is still quite cool. The exception to this is the Peruvian penguin which can be found right along the coasts of Chile and Peru, where a cold current of water sweeps up towards the Equator. The Galapagos penguin lives even on the Galapagos Islands, just on the Equator.

With the emperor penguin, the Adélie is confined to the Antarctic continent and its neighbouring islands. Other species, including the chinstrap, gentoo and macaroni penguins, live around the fringes of the continent and on the islands; but their main breeding grounds are farther to the north, in sub-Antarctic and temperate latitudes.

The penguin is a flightless gregarious bird; a superb swimmer, it is completely adapted to life in water; the wings having evolved into flippers, and the body become covered with a protective layer of blubber. Its progress on land seems comically clumsy when compared with the efficient grace with which it moves through the water.

Many penguins have distinctive colouring around the head, sometimes with plumes or crests of orange feathers. But the Adélie penguin, which stands about 18 in. tall, is simply coloured, with a white belly and black back and throat. The eye is distinguished by a surrounding circle of white that gives the bird the appearance of a golliwog.

The pengun is a flightless bird, its wings having evolved into flippers.

Antarctic environment

On a September or October day on the edge of the Antarctic continent, with the sea frozen as far as the eye can see, quite suddenly, a line of dots might appear, moving in a straight line across the ice. Each dot seems to be gliding along as if pulled by a string, until it reaches a crack in the ice when some of the dots suddenly change shape. A closer inspection would show them to be Adélie penguins which have been tobogganing over the ice on their bellies, using their feet and flippers to propel themselves. When they reached the crack they stood up to get a better view across it. After a bit of jostling they walk to the edge of the crack, waddling on their ridiculously short legs, and holding out their flippers for balance. Eventually they jump across and resume their slow progress.

These penguins are on their way to the nesting grounds, or rookeries, where they nest in thousands. They have spent the long winter on the edges of the frozen seas where there is an abundance of food and they are now in prime condition, their bodies padded with half an inch of blubber and their feathers sleek and glossy. At first the groups consist of a dozen or so penguins, but they increase in numbers until streams of penguins are flowing in towards the rookeries.

From rookery to crèche

At the rookery, which is usually situated on a rocky headland, each penguin searches for its old nest, or if it is breeding for the first time, finds an empty space. The nests are still covered with snow, but the penguins know exactly where to look for them. The males usually arrive first and they stand on the nest, fighting off other males and waiting for their mates. They have a special display that at once intimidates other males and attracts females. It is called the 'ecstatic display': the penguin points his bill to the sky, waves his flippers to and fro and utters a loud braying call.

When all the penguins have arrived and the pairs have formed it can be seen that each penguin sitting on its future nest is exactly the same distance from each of its neighbours. This even spreading ensures that they do not interfere with each other too much and that the eggs and chicks will not be disturbed. Occasionally a penguin does get in the way of its neighbours and a fight breaks out. Penguins fight by pecking and by beating with their flippers.

When the snow melts, nest-building can begin. The male collects pebbles which he takes one at a time to the female, who remains standing on the nest site. He drops each pebble in turn at her feet and she uses them to build up a ring around her. Usually the pebbles are laboriously collected from the beach, but the penguins miss no chance to steal them from any unguarded nest.

Two white eggs, each 2 in. long, are laid in the nest of pebbles; the male broods them while the female goes back to the sea to feed – for she will not have eaten for two or three weeks. A fortnight later she returns, while the male goes off to break his fast of some six weeks, during which he will have lost almost half his weight. The eggs hatch after 36 days and for the first few days the chicks stay under their parents.

While one parent is guarding the chicks the other collects food for them, returning with it stored in the crop where it is partly digested. Reaching the nest, the adult penguin opens its beak to the chick. The chick then pushes its head into the adult's mouth to take the food that is disgorged.

The chicks grow rapidly, coming out from under the parents to stand by the nest. Then, when a month old, they leave the nest to gather in groups called *crèches*, from the French word for public nurseries. It was once thought that the adult penguins that stood around the crèches were special guardians, looking after the chicks while the parents were away feeding; but it is now known that they are birds that have lost their eggs and are just standing around.

Once the chicks have joined the circles the adults do not simply walk up and feed them. Instead they lead the chicks away from the crèche, making them run over the rocks and then make their way back again after they have been fed. One function of this is to introduce the chicks to the outside world, for soon they will be leaving the crèche and taking to the sea.

▷ *The penguin's progress on land seems comically clumsy when compared with its graceful movement in water.*

▽ *Adélie penguins tobogganing over the ice on their bellies, using feet and flippers to propel themselves.*

Lewis Smith

Lewis Smith

△ *Nests are built by the female from pebbles brought by the male, and each pair has its own nest territory, evenly spaced from the next. This penguin 'rookery' includes an albino and a pair of chinstrap penguins.*

▷ *Month old Adélies leave the nest to live in crèches.*

Anthony

Lewis Smith

Crustacean feeder

It is at first sight surprising to find colonies of thousands of penguins in the apparently desolate wastes of the Antarctic; but in contrast with the land, the Antarctic seas are teeming with life—especially with the small shrimp-like creatures such as amphipods and krill on which the penguins, as well as the seals and whales, feed. The reason for this abundance of food lies in the circulation of the oceans. Moving southwards toward Antarctica, there is a current that flows along the ocean beds. In it are the salts, such as phosphates and nitrates, that are brought down to the seas in rivers and are also released when dead animals from the surface layers sink and decompose. On reaching the cold Antarctic this warm current, rich in nutrient salts, wells up to the surface and the salts nourish myriads of minute planktonic plants. These in turn nourish the small animals on which the penguins feed.

Skua and leopard seal enemies

There are no land animals in the Antarctic to menace the rookeries, but a predatory sea bird, the great skua, breeds near the rookeries, and takes the eggs and chicks of the penguins whenever the opportunity arises. They wait for a penguin to neglect its eggs for a second and swoop down to carry one away in the bill. Sometimes a pair of skuas will work together, one attracting the penguin's attention while the other sneaks up behind to steal an egg. Later, the skuas wait around the crèches for a chick to become separated from its fellows. The skuas are unable to kill a healthy chick but can harass a weakened one until it succumbs.

Both adults and the young are in danger from leopard seals as they enter the water. Again a healthy alert bird will probably be safe from them and the seals have to be content with chasing weakly penguins.

Selfish and callous?

There is a story of Adélie penguins which seems to credit them not only with a high level of intelligence but with a selfishness

▷ *Adélie penguins are gregarious birds living on the Antarctic continent and its neighbouring islands.*

▷ *An Adélie penguin stands 18 in. high*

C.Herbert: British Antarctic Survey

Russ Kinne: Photo Res.

that is rivalled only by the most callous of humans. The story as usually told is that the penguins will go to the edge of the ice, line up along it and then push one of their number into the water. If that one comes to the surface again all go in, because they then know there are no leopard seals about. If the unfortunate one that has been ducked does not surface, they know a leopard seal has eaten it and all turn round and walk away, postponing their fishing until later.

On the face of it this seems too extraordinary a story to swallow, and yet it has been reported again and again even by serious zoologists. It seems the story was brought back by the early Antarctic explorers and particularly by Ponting, the

photographer on Scott's expedition to the Antarctic, who lectured widely on his return.

A simpler explanation is much more likely. When a crowd of penguins are walking across the ice and come to an obstacle, for example, a wide crack in the ice, all will stop and inspect it. There is a good deal of jostling, and any penguin that is pushed to the edge tries to get away and run round to the back of the crowd. They may even do the same if they come to a hump in the ice. After this exploration one of them will in due course jump across the crack and the others stream after it: penguins tend to behave like a flock of sheep and will stand around until one of them starts moving.

It is easy to see that if this sort of thing

happened at the edge of the ice a penguin might go into the water of its own volition; but it might look as if it had been pushed. Anyone seeing this, who did not have the advantage of the increased knowledge of penguins and of animal behaviour that we have today could very readily misinterpret what he had seen.

class	**Aves**
order	**Sphenisciformes**
family	**Spheniscidae**
genus & species	***Pygoscelis adeliae***

17

Agama

A genus of about 50 lizards belonging to the family Agamidae, which is related to the iguanas and includes in its 200 species such types as the Australian moloch or thorny devil, the frilled lizard and the flying dragons. The best known agama is the foot-long common agama of Africa, Agama agama. The male agama's head is bright terracotta, the colour of the African earth; his body and legs are dark blue; his tail banded pale blue, white, orange and black. His skin is rough to the touch, like sandpaper, and he has a dewlap of loose skin under his chin and a row of small spines on his neck like the comb of a young cock.

Other members of the genus include the starred agama (A. stellio) of the eastern Mediterranean region, and the desert agama (A. mutabilis) of North Africa. Among other genera of agamids not separately treated in this work are: Phrynocephalus (about 40 species, the toad-headed agamids), Calotes (about 25 species), Uromastix (spiny-tailed lizards), Hydrosaurus (water lizard).

Green crested lizard (Calotes cristatellus) *of south-east Asia, one of the Agamid family.*

African distribution and habits

Agamas are the commonest reptiles in West Africa. Anyone who sets foot there cannot fail to notice them within the first few minutes. They are seen wherever the forest and bush have been cleared. In villages they run up and down hut walls, scamper across compounds and clatter over corrugated iron roofs, while in the main streets of the big towns thronged with people and traffic, they sunbathe in decorative groups on walls of modern stores or on ruins of houses—an urban rabble in their rubble slums.

At first sight there seems to be a confusing variety of other lizards as well. They can be seen in all sizes from five inches to a foot—some sandy, some chocolate, some with green-spotted heads, some with orange blotches on their sides. But it soon becomes clear that they are all the same species, the smallest being hatchlings, the middle-sizes females, and the largest of all, males. Only mature males that are dominant—that is, strong enough to boss other males—maintain the bright orange-and-blue colouring. Weak or subordinate males, or any that have had a bad fright, are dull brown. The mature male agama with his red face and ferocious mien looks extraordinarily like the traditional picture of a peppery colonel about to explode in an apoplectic fit.

The common agama has adapted its ways to become a companion of man, living in the thatch of huts, emerging to feed on scraps and insects, but always ready to race back to shelter if disturbed. If caught in the open it is able to run on its hind legs.

During the day the lizards are extremely active, hurtling across open spaces from one heap of stones to another, darting out to snap up ants, even leaping into the air after flying insects. Only in the afternoon, when the temperature reaches around 37·8°C/100°F in the shade, do they try to find a cool spot in which to lie down. As soon as it becomes a little cooler they begin to chase about again.

They seem to be always quarrelling. Fights are constantly breaking out between the colourful males. When two rivals catch sight of one another, both will repeatedly raise and lower the front part of the body in an extremely comical bobbing action, as if they were doing jerky press-ups. If the contestants are equally matched they will quickly come to blows, lashing out at each other with their strong tails and threatening with open jaws. Many of the large males have shortened or broken tails, the result of such fights. Even the females chase and fight each other, and sometimes the tiny hatchling lizards play at fighting, as kittens and puppies do.

Towards dusk the agamas congregate in communal roosts, often in the eaves of houses, and at night all the males, regardless of their social standing, go a dull brown colour all over, like the subordinate males. But the next morning, when out in the early sun, their brilliant colours return.

The desert agama lives in the dry areas of North Africa, avoiding bare sand. After the cold night an agama will be literally stiff with cold, but with the sunrise it absorbs energy and its temperature rises so that it can start hunting, courting and so on. As the sun's power increases the desert agama must be careful not to overheat—although it can tolerate greater temperatures than most reptiles. The sparse scrub of the desert gives sufficient shelter to the agamas, who dash from one bush to another as they go about their daily business.

Insectivorous feeders

Agamas are mainly insectivorous, chasing their prey at speed and catching small insects with the tongue or snapping up larger ones directly with the mouth. The incisor-like front teeth are pointed like those of insectivorous mammals. Agamas may also eat grass, berries, seeds and the eggs of smaller lizards.

Polygamous breeder

The common agama is polygamous. The brilliantly coloured male may be seen with half a dozen or more females, in a territory which he defends vigorously.

In courtship the male comes alongside the female, bobbing his head, and then, if she allows him, grips her neck with his jaws. If she is out of breeding condition and does not allow this, he will continue bobbing until exhausted. If he is successful, he puts one hind leg over her back, grasps her hind leg with his foot, and twists the hind end of his body under her. The female then raises her tail away from the male and the vents are brought together.

Sometimes the female initiates the courtship by running up to the male and raising her tail in front of him. He then chases her until she lets him catch up.

△ *A male African common agama, bobbing his head in boundary threat display. The bright red head is a sign of his aggressiveness.*

▽ Agama bibroni *grows to about 10 in. from nose to tip of tail. Here the dull brownish colour suggests it is of inferior rank.*

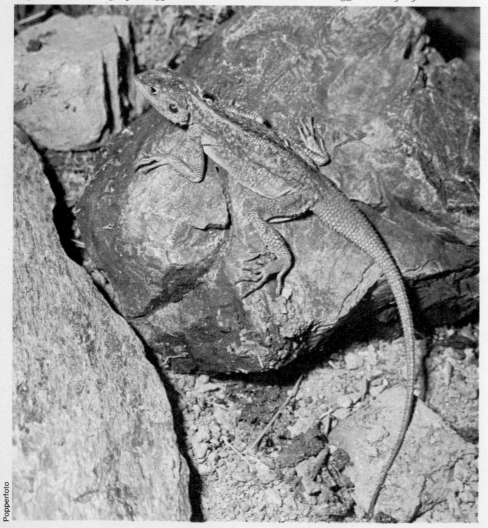

Even common agamas living near the Equator have a very definite breeding season, which occurs after the 'long rains' of March-May. The males have ripe spermatozoa all the year, but the females can only lay eggs from June to September, some months after the rains. At this time the vegetation becomes lush and the insect population rises, providing the female agamas with an ample supply of protein for the formation of eggs, which are then laid in clutches of up to twelve.

The peppery colonel

The reference to peppery colonels is not without point, for agamas have their little empires to defend. In rural districts they are well spaced out, each male owning his country estate. By watching the different males it is easy to pick out each one's stronghold: a tree, a log or a rock near the middle of his territory. You can then draw fairly accurate lines marking the boundaries of these territories, and along these lines the owners battle to maintain or extend their properties.

In the towns, where agamas are thicker on the ground, the territorial instinct can lead to more frequent fighting and to situations which appear to us somewhat comic.

An illustration of this is an actual situation observed in Akure in West Africa. Close to a bungalow lived a fine male agama, readily recognisable because he had a clubbed tail, having lost an inch of tip. He was nicknamed Old Apoplexy—Apo for short—by an English family occupying the bungalow. His territory included a strip of grass with four trees and a hedge to one side. He basked much of his time beside his three 'wives', but was often engaged in fights with a neighbouring agama, 'Rival', who had five wives.

Rival had to patrol the other boundaries of his territory, and while he was absent Apo would rush in and grab one of his females, beating a speedy retreat when Rival returned. One day he failed to make a quick enough getaway. Rival drove him up a tree, higher and higher, until he lost sight of Apo, who faded to a dull grey as his fighting spirit ebbed. But Rival, after descending the tree, waited at the base for Apo.

By the following day a third male had taken over Apo's territory, and two mornings later he was still in possession. In the afternoon a club-tailed male agama, chocolate in colour, entered this territory. It was Apo, who had at last escaped. Suddenly there was a muddle of flailing feet and tails. The third lizard, caught off balance, retreated as fast as he could. Gradually, Apo, back victorious on his own territory and lord once more of three wives, changed from chocolate to grey flecked with green, and his head resumed its orange tint.

class	**Reptilia**
order	**Squamata** *suborder Sauria*
family	**Agamidae**
genera	***Agama*** *and others*

△ *Agoutis are delicate eaters, sitting back on their haunches and holding their food in the fore feet, sometimes even peeling it.*

▽ *Hunted agoutis will make for water when hard pressed. They are good swimmers but cannot dive.*

Agouti

A genus of Central and South American rodents resembling large, long-legged guinea pigs. The numerous species vary in colour from tawny to blackish-brown with lighter underparts. One species has white stripes. The coarse hair is longer on the hind quarters, where it is usually bright orange or golden but may be white or black. This hair is raised when the animal is alarmed or aggressive. The head is rather rat-like, with relatively large, pinkish ears. The agouti is about 20 in. long, with a short, hairless tail and long legs. It has five toes on the fore feet and three on the hind feet; all have hooflike claws.

A close relative of the agouti is the acouchi of north-western South America (Myoprocta pratti). The principal difference is that the acouchi has a slender, white-tipped tail which is used as a signal in courting ceremonies.

South American distribution

Agoutis are abundant in forest and wooded areas throughout Central and South America from Mexico southwards to Brazil and Peru: one species is found in the Antilles. Where they are undisturbed agoutis are said to be diurnal; but they are mostly known as nocturnal animals that spend the day in holes in trees or in burrows scraped in the ground among soft limestone boulders or under the roots of trees.

The burrows are shallow 'foxholes', 2–3 ft deep, sometimes roofed over by a lattice of twigs covered with leaves. Each burrow is occupied by one animal or a small group probably consisting of a family. Well-worn tracks radiate from the entrance to the communal feeding ground.

Reports differ as to whether agoutis are social or solitary in their way of life; different species may well have different habits. It seems that, although they sleep in their burrows alone or in small groups, they gather in groups of up to 100 to feed. It is also said that they are very shy and 'highly strung'—fighting fiercely among themselves yet fleeing in panic at the first alarm, even jumping over cliffs *en masse*.

Despite these conflicting characteristics—fighting and fleeing—agoutis are easily tamed and make affectionate pets. They can live up to 20 years, but the average length of life is six years.

Feeding

Like all rodents agoutis are mainly vegetarians, browsing on leaves, fallen fruit and roots. Sometimes they climb trees to take green fruit. They are delicate eaters, sitting back on their haunches and holding their food in the fore feet and, if it has a tough skin, peeling it carefully with their teeth before eating it. They hoard food in small stores buried near landmarks.

Occasionally they eat the eggs of ground-nesting birds, and have even been seen searching for shellfish on the seashore.

Three-toed runner

The agouti, unlike its relatives such as the guinea pig, is adapted for fast running. This drawing of an orange rumped agouti shows its long legs and the three toes on the hind feet which give minimum contact with the ground and maximum leverage.

Barry Driscoll

Breeding

Litters number from two to six; in the wild two is the most common, in zoos, one. Some species have two litters each year, in May and October; others appear to breed all the year round. The young are born in a burrow lined with leaves, roots and hair. Their arrival is unusual in that the mother gives birth while in a squatting position. They are quite well developed at birth: they are covered with hair, their eyes are open, and within an hour they are nibbling at vegetation. This advanced stage of development is linked with the long gestation period of three months.

While the young are very small the father is barred from the nest. They remain with the parents for some weeks.

Enemies

On being disturbed the agouti first freezes to avoid being detected (the young have this ability from birth): it sits with body upright and ankles flat on the ground ready to leap off at full speed. This it then does, screaming shrilly and dodging obstacles with remarkable agility.

Agoutis have been described as the 'basic diet of South American carnivores' such as the ocelot and the jaguar. Man also finds in agoutis a plentiful source of food, and they are hunted too in areas where they are pests of sugar cane and banana plantations.

One neat hunter's trick is to toss stones into the air. These, falling through the leaves and hitting the ground, sound to the agoutis like falling fruit, and so they come out to feed. Another hunting method depends on the agoutis' habit of making for water when hard pressed. They are good swimmers but cannot dive. So beaters drive the agoutis towards a river, where they are easy targets for hunters lying in wait.

Adapted for running

Agoutis are fast runners, escaping predators by speed rather than by hiding in burrows. They are very agile and bound through undergrowth undaunted by precipices, on which they display the agility of goats. Leaps of 20 ft from a standing start have been recorded.

This is surprising behaviour for an animal related to such pedestrian creatures as guinea pigs and porcupines. The reason lies in the anatomical features that distinguish the agouti from its relatives, namely its long, thin legs and the hoof-like claws on which it walks and gallops—so resembling the ungulates or hoofed mammals. The latter have become adapted for running by the development of long legs, the reduction in the number of toes and the formation of hooves—the number of toes being reduced by the animal's feet being raised so that fewer toes touch the ground. There has been a similar trend in the agoutis, resulting in long legs and the three-toed hind feet. This situation is similar to a stage in the evolution of the horse from a five-toed ancestor to the modern single-hoofed horse.

class	**Mammalia**
order	**Rodentia**
family	**Dasyproctidae**
genus	*Dasyprocta*

Alaska blackfish

A fish that lives in freshwater pools, streams and marshes in north-western Alaska, on a few islands in the Bering Straits and in Siberia. It is seldom found far inland, but where it does occur it is abundant and serves as food for the Eskimo and his dog. One observer has told of seeing the water courses leading from lagoons almost blocked with blackfish. The fish itself is unpretentious. It is somberly coloured — greyish with irregular black bars — and reaches a maximum length of about 8 in. It is chubby and somewhat pike-like with its jutting lower jaw; some scientists maintain that it is related to pikes. It is, however, sufficiently unlike other fishes to be placed in a family on its own.

The Alaska blackfish has for many years been the subject of controversy as to its apparent ability to survive in blocks of ice.

△ *The Alaska blackfish is about 8 in. long. The large gills, protected by gill covers, help it to survive in adverse conditions.*

▽ *A weed-choked pond in a sphagnum bog, like those in which the blackfish makes its summer home.*

Sluggish freshwater dweller

In winter the Alaska blackfish lives in deep water, perhaps as deep as 20 ft, and moves back into depths of a few inches in the spring. In the summer it lives among dense growths of water plants and never enters clear water. It is not an active fish, although it can move at lightning speed when alarmed — reminiscent of a frog leaping from a hand put out to grasp it.

The blackfish seems to be specialised for surviving adverse conditions. In winter it lives below the ice at temperatures approaching 0°C/32°F, while in summer the water reaches about 20°C/68°F. It is also tolerant of overcrowding to a far greater degree than most other fishes: it can stand up to competition with other species as well, both in the matter of living space and food; and it can exist in water with low oxygen content. It is perhaps this hardiness which gave rise to some of the less credible tales of survival in extreme conditions.

Food

It was once thought that the Alaska black-fish lived on plants and worms. Later studies show that it does eat both these to a slight extent, as well as small crustaceans known as water fleas; its main food, however, is insect larvae, especially those of the two-winged flies such as midges and mosquitoes.

Breeding

The blackfish spawns in June and July, and in May and June the males develop a reddish margin to the fins. There seems to be no elaborate courtship or parental care of the eggs. The fry grow quickly and the young fishes are chestnut-brown with white bellies and dark brown bars on the flanks.

The old, old, story

There is an old myth that certain animals, including the Alaska blackfish, can be frozen alive in a block of ice and revived when the ice is melted. As regards the blackfish, the myth seems to have started with a statement in Sir John Franklin's book, *First Overland Journey to Polar Seas*, about carp completely frozen being thawed before a fire and 're-covering their animation'. This was in 1824; in 1882 Nordensjöld, in his *Voyage of the Vega*, reported fishes living in a lagoon that froze to the bottom. He later modified this to 'apparently freezes' to the bottom. Four years later L. M. Turner, who explored Alaska, spoke of fish frozen in grass baskets for weeks being brought into the house, thawed out and found to be as lively as ever. He also told the story of a frozen fish thrown to one of the Eskimo dogs being swallowed and vomited up after a short while, when it was found to have been revived by the warmth of the dog's stomach.

Most laymen and many scientists swallowed these stories. But there were sceptics also, and before many years had passed investigators were using the newly invented cold stores to test them. The Russian, Borodin, was the first to be disillusioned, as the result of extensive tests carried out prior to 1934. Since then the American Scholander and his associates have found they were unable to freeze blackfish and have them survive. Another American, Walters, put some blackfish into a small pond in Alaska which he knew would freeze solid in winter. The fish did not survive.

The truth is that the story of the black-fish, including that of the one vomited by the Eskimo dog — which few writers on the fish have failed to repeat — are founded on Eskimo folk-lore. Yet it is because the stories are so near to being possible that they have been so hard to refute. Goldfish, carp, tench and other species — and the blackfish — can be supercooled and still survive — under certain conditions. They can be subjected to temperatures below freezing point and, provided no ice crystals come in contact with the body, they can be re-suscitated. Borodin found that the blackfish, for example, can survive 30 – 35 minutes exposure to −20°C/−36°F but that an hour's exposure is fatal. It should be emphasised, however, that such exposure must be in super-cooled dry air where no ice crystals can form. In other experiments it has been shown that freezing — in the true sense — even a part of the body of a blackfish results in necrosis — that is, the affected tissues are damaged beyond repair.

class	**Pisces**
order	**Haplomi**
family	**Dalliidae**
genus & species	***Dallia pectoralis***

Albatross

A family of birds in the petrel order. They are the largest members of the order and among the largest of flying birds. They have goose-sized bodies with very long, slender wings: of the 13 species, the largest is the wandering albatross, which has a wingspan sometimes exceeding 12 ft. The plumage is black and white or, in a few species, brown. In only some of the species is it possible to tell the sexes apart.

1. Yellow-nosed albatross (Diomedea chlororhyncha) *landing,* showing its large wingspan. This enables it to soar for hours in the oceanic air currents.
2. The albatross nests on cliff tops where it can easily take off. The chick is guarded by its parents for several weeks.
3. Later both parents can be away feeding for ten days at a time.
4. Black-browed albatross (Diomedea melano-phrys) *ranges over the oceans between 30° and 60° latitude south, breeding on such islands as Tristan da Cunha, South Georgia, and the Kerguelen and Auckland Islands. It has been recorded as a vagrant to the British Isles and even to the Arctic. The wandering albatross* (D. exulans) *can live for over 30 years and may weigh 17 lb with a wingspan up to 12 ft.*

Ocean wanderers

Nine species of albatross are confined to the Southern Hemisphere, breeding mainly on the sub-Antarctic and oceanic islands. The other four are found in the North Pacific. None breed in the North Atlantic, although fossil remains have been found in England and a few have been recorded as vagrants in modern times. These vagrants include wandering, black-browed, yellow-nosed, grey-headed, and light-mantled sooty albatrosses. One black-browed albatross appeared in a Faroese gannet colony in 1860 and for 30 years—until it was shot—it accompanied the gannets on their annual migrations. Another visited the Bass Rock gannet colony off the Scottish coast in 1967 and returned in 1968.

The doldrums, the windless belt around the Equator, are possibly one of the reasons why so few albatrosses have been recorded in the North Atlantic, as albatrosses need a sustained wind for flight. They are heavy birds with comparatively small wing muscles, but they can remain airborne for long periods and cover vast distances because of the difference in the speed of the wind at the water's surface and some 50 ft above, due to friction slowing down the air at the surface. The albatross glides swiftly downwind and surfacewards, gathering speed. When just above the water it swings sharply round into the wind and soars up. As it rises it loses momentum and its ground speed (*i.e.* in relation to the water surface) decreases. Its air speed, however, does not decrease so fast, as the bird is rising and so continually meeting faster wind currents. By the time the air speed has dropped completely the albatross will have gained sufficient height to start the downward glide again. Thus it progresses in a series of zig-zags.

The main haunt of albatrosses is the sub-Antarctic zone where the Roaring Forties and Howling Fifties sweep around the world and there is nearly always enough wind to keep the albatrosses aloft—although they can glide in quite gentle breezes. To increase speed the albatross 'close-hauls', partly closing its wings to reduce air resistance without seriously affecting lift.

With their great wingspan and weak wing muscles albatrosses have difficulty in taking off. When there is enough wind—especially if there are thermal currents or eddies around the cliffs on which they nest—takeoff is not so difficult; but on still days they have to taxi, running along and flapping their wings until they have gained sufficient air speed to take off.

Some species are fairly confined in their range, like Buller's albatross in New Zealand; others, like the wandering, black-browed and sooty albatrosses circle the world from Tropics to Antarctic.

Marine feeders

All species of albatross feed on marine organisms living at the surface of the sea, such as fish, squid and crustaceans. They also take small sea birds on occasions, and they like refuse from ships, flopping down into the water as soon as a bucketful is tipped overboard. Sailors who have fallen overboard have reputedly been viciously attacked by albatrosses.

Cliff top breeding sites

Breeding grounds, where albatrosses gather in tens of thousands, are usually on the top of cliffs where the birds can take off easily. They are extremely faithful to their nest sites, and populations have survived such calamities as volcanic eruptions or pillage by man because the immature birds that were absent at the time later returned to breed.

Albatrosses are very long-lived birds: one recaptured 19 years after being ringed as an adult must have been at least 26 years old. They do not start breeding until at least seven years old, but young birds return to the breeding ground before then and court halfheartedly. Courtship displays, which are to be seen throughout the breeding season, are most spectacular. The two birds of a pair dance grotesquely and awkwardly with outstretched wings to the accompaniment of nasal groans and bill snapping. At the beginning of the breeding season several males may dance around one female.

A single egg is laid in a cup shaped nest of mud and is incubated by both parents for periods ranging from 65 days in the smaller species to 81 days in the larger ones. The chick is also brooded for a short time and is guarded by the adults for several weeks. It is then left by itself and both parents can be away feeding at once. They return every 10 days to give the chick a huge meal of regurgitated squid and fish. The young of the smaller albatrosses fledge in two to three months, but larger ones may spend eight or nine months in the colony, sitting out the severe southern winter until the following summer. The parents feed them the whole time, so breeding is only possible in alternate years.

The young albatrosses leave the breeding grounds to glide away around the world, driven by the winds of the Westerly Drift. Before they return to start courting several years later they may circle the globe many times.

No natural enemies

Albatrosses have no natural enemies, living as they do on remote islands. Any introduced carnivores would, however, wreak havoc among the densely packed nests, for the sitting albatross's reaction to disturbance is just to sit tight on the nest and clack its bill. It also spits oil from digested crustaceans and fish—as does the chick—but this is hardly likely to discourage a determined predator.

The sailors' curse

Albatrosses have been known to sailors since the days of Magellan. Their inexpressive, fixed facial expression as they glide alongside a ship for miles on end without a flicker of the eye has brought them various nicknames: Mollymawk (from the Dutch Mallemok, 'stupid gull'), Gooney (English/American for a stupid person), Bakadori (Japanese for 'fowl-birds').

But they not only had a reputation for idiocy; they were considered to be harbingers of wind and storms—not, perhaps, surprising in view of their difficulty in remaining aloft in calm weather. They were

△ *The albatross glides swiftly downwind and surfacewards, gathering speed. When just above the water it swings sharply round into the wind and soars up.*
▽ *The albatross's great wingspan is supported by relatively small muscles as it rarely flaps its wings. It remains airborne for long periods, gliding vast distances using the updraught above crests.*

also regarded as the reincarnations of seamen washed overboard, and it was thought extremely unlucky to kill them, as Coleridge expressed in his *Ancient Mariner*:

> *And I had done an hellish thing*
> *And it would work 'em woe:*
> *For all averr'd, I had kill'd the Bird*
> *That made the Breeze to blow.*

But, despite the chance of having an albatross hung round one's neck and suffering the far worse experience that later befell the Ancient Mariner, sailors have not always treated albatrosses kindly. Their capture on baited hooks trailed from the stern of a ship often relieved the monotony of life and diet.

More seriously, albatrosses were once favourite material for the 19th-century millinery trade, the wings sometimes being cut off the still-living birds. The North Pacific colonies bore the brunt of this fashion for plumage which, luckily, ceased before all the birds were dead.

Since the Second World War there has been another crisis for the albatross. Long-range aircraft flights have made oceanic islands necessary as staging posts, and one such is Midway Island, the home of the Laysan albatross. Not only are albatrosses using the United States Navy's runways for taking off, they also soar in the thermals above them, providing a serious danger to aircraft. Of the many methods that have been tried to reduce this danger, the most effective has been the bulldozing of dunes by the runways which cause the updraughts that the albatrosses need for flying.

class	**Aves**
order	**Procellariiformes**
family	**Diomedeidae**
genus	*Diomedea spp.*
& species	*Phoebetria spp.*

Alder-fly

A primitive insect whose larvae live in water. It is not a true fly, like the housefly, but belongs to a group of insects which includes the lace-wings and ant-lions. This group reached its zenith during the times when the coal measures were being laid down, 300 million years ago.

The adult insect has a body about 1 in. in length, long antennae and dull, heavily veined wings. When the insect is at rest the wings are folded over the back and ridged like a house roof. They are little known, if not wholly unfamiliar to most people, but are well known to the fly fishermen as one of the 'flies' used for trout.

Habits

The adult insect flies little—almost reluct-antly—but when it takes off the flight is direct. More usually it rests or crawls on plants or stones near a water's edge. Its life is short—merely long enough to ensure the laying of a batch of eggs. The most striking feature of the larvae is its gills, designed for breathing under water, of which there are seven pairs on the abdomen. They look like extra legs, each being made up of a series of five joints clothed with bristles, except that they are held upwards and backwards. A further un-paired gill is carried at the end of the body. The larva spends much of its time under stones and pebbles but can swim freely by undulating its body. When the oxygen content of the water is low the larva will undulate its body in the same way while remaining stationary, so causing a current of water to flow over the gills. This is of considerable value, especially to those species of alder-fly that live in muddy or stagnant water, which lacks the aeration of a running stream.

Life cycle

In March each female lays up to 2,000 brown, cigar-shaped eggs on plants or stones near water. These stand on end in flat masses, each of 200—500 eggs, like commuters on a station platform. They hatch in two weeks and the larvae make their way to water. The larval stage of life usually lasts for two years, during which the brown larva grows to 1 in. long. During May and June the full-term larvae leave the water and may travel some distance before making an oval cell in mud or vegetable debris in which to pupate. One was seen to travel 6 yd, apparently having climbed over a concrete wall and through a cotoneaster thicket to an open flower bed. Three weeks later the pupa leaves its cell and from it the adult insect emerges.

In many insect pupae the legs and wings are inside the pupal case. In the alder-fly pupa they are already free of the body but in special sheaths; as is usual in pupae that have to make their way to the surface before the adult insect emerges, there are spines on the abdominal ridges.

Alder-fly on alder leaves. It never eats during its few days of life as its larva has lived and eaten for at least a year.

Anglers use the larvae of alder-flies as bait. But they are valuable to fishermen in another way, as well as to the economy of the streams, for they and other insect larvae make possible the existence of fish such as trout. They are an important link in the food chain of water creatures, being converters of protein. Plants manufacture food; small animals feed on plants; the larvae of alder-flies feed on these vegetarian animals such as the larvae of caddis-flies; thus trout and bass, which eat the alder-fly larvae, gain protein. So the larvae are the main support of the fishes which the fisherman catches even though he uses the adult as bait. Normally adult alder-flies alight on water only when they fall from overhanging vegetation—when suddenly disturbed by a bird flying near, or when blown down by a gust of wind.

A second point of interest is one that applies to many insects—the adult is short-lived. It serves only for reproducing and dispersing the species. The male, having fertilised the female, serves no other purpose except as food for other animals. It is the same with the female once she has laid her eggs. The 'real' life of the insect is in the larva, which is longer-lived and is adapted to an entirely different way of life.

Feeding

The adult does not feed. The larva is carnivorous and seizes any small animals that come its way with its vicious, pincer-like mouthparts, or mandibles.

27

△ *The alder-fly larva is divided into segments, each with a pair of jointed appendages. Those on the head form the vicious jaws; three pairs on the thorax form legs; and those on the abdomen are gills (× 12).*

▽ *The female alder fly lays her eggs in close-packed rows, like commuters on a station.*

Reluctant aeronaut

When authors write of a reluctance on the part of the adult alder-fly to take wing, they are referring to the manner in which the insect will, on being disturbed, run quickly up a leaf or a stem, then fly directly to a nearby leaf or stem, and merely repeat this manoeuvre whenever disturbed.

It is very likely that this behaviour of the alder-fly gives us an important clue to the origin and evolution of flight in insects. The alder-fly is primitive in other ways and it is not unreasonable to suppose that its flying behaviour is also primitive. We have seen how the larvae live for a year or two while the adult has only a short-lived existence, taking no food and living just long enough to mate and for the female to lay her eggs. Flight can have no value for food capture, because no food is eaten. There is no question of migration. Consequently, the two primary purposes of flight in the alder-fly are to bring the sexes together and to make possible evasive action to escape enemies long enough for the eggs to be fertilised and laid.

In the course of insect evolution other functions have been added. For example, bees, wasps and dragonflies use flight to get food. Many insects migrate—some butterflies migrate from the Sahara to Scotland. Nevertheless, it must be emphasised that the two primary purposes of flight in insects are to ensure mating and to provide protection from enemies, with a third but subsidiary function—that of spreading the species. In the case of the alder-fly this spread could only be very slow.

All this contrasts strongly with the function of flight in birds and bats, where it plays such a large part in food capture and security and is often a way to avoid the worst rigours of climate by migration.

class	**Insecta**
order	**Neuroptera**
genus & species	***Sialis spp.***

When annoyed, alligators open their vast jaws and roar. Male alligators also roar during their quarrels in the breeding season and to attract females.

Alligator

Two species of reptiles which, with the caimans, belong to a family closely related to the crocodiles. Alligators and crocodiles look extremely alike: the main distinguishing feature is the teeth.
In a crocodile the teeth in the upper and lower jaws are in line, but in the alligator, when its mouth is shut, the upper teeth lie outside the lower. In both animals the fourth lower tooth on each side is perceptibly larger than the rest: in the crocodile this tooth fits into a notch in the upper jaw and is visible when the mouth is closed, whereas in the alligator, with the lower teeth inside the upper, it fits into a pit in the upper jaw and is lost to sight when the mouth is shut. In addition, the alligator's head is broader and shorter and the snout consequently blunter. Otherwise, especially in their adaptations to an aquatic life, alligators are very similar to crocodiles.
One of the two species is found in North America, the other in China. The Chinese alligator averages a little over 4 ft in length and has no webs between the toes. The American alligator is much larger, with a maximum recorded length of 19 ft 2 in. This length, however, is seldom attained nowadays because the American alligator has been killed off for the sake of its skin; whenever there is intense persecution of an animal the larger ones are quickly

eliminated and the average size of the remainder drops slowly as persecution proceeds.
It is sheer accident that two such similar reptiles as the alligator and the crocodile should so early have been given different common names. The reason is that when the Spanish seamen, who had presumably no knowledge of crocodiles, first saw large reptiles in the Central American rivers, they spoke of them as lizards—el largato in Spanish. The English sailors who followed later adopted the Spanish name but ran the two into one to make 'allagarter'—which was later further corrupted to 'alligator'.

Long lazy life
Alligators are more sluggish than crocodiles; this may possibly have an effect on their longevity, for there are records of alligators having lived more than 50 years. They spend most of their time basking on the banks of rivers.

The American alligator is restricted to the south-eastern United States and does not penetrate further north than latitude 35. The Chinese alligator is found only in the Yangtse River basin.

Meat eaters
Alligators' food changes with age. The young feed on insects and on those crustaceans generally known as freshwater shrimps. As they grow older they eat frogs, snakes and fish; mature adults live mainly on fish but will catch muskrats and small mammals that go down to the water's edge to drink. They also take a certain amount of waterfowl. Very large alligators may

occasionally pull large mammals such as deer or cows down into the water and drown them.

Alligator builds a nest
It seems that the female alligator plays the more active role in courtship and territorial defence. The males apparently spend much of the breeding season quarrelling among themselves, roaring and fighting and injuring each other. The roaring attracts the females to the males, as does a musky secretion from glands in the male's throat and cloaca. Courtship takes place usually at night, the pair swimming round faster and faster and finally mating in the water with jaws interlocked and the male's body arched over the female's.

A large nest-mound is made for the reception of the eggs. The female scoops up mud in her jaws and mixes it with decaying vegetation; the mixture is then deposited on the nest site until a mound 3 ft high is made. The eggs are hard-shelled and number 15—80; they are laid in a depression in the top of the mound and covered with more vegetation. The female remains by the eggs until they hatch 2—3 months later, incubated by the heat of the nest's rotting vegetation.

The hatchling alligators peep loudly and the female removes the layer of vegetation over the nest to help them escape. Baby alligators are 8 in. long when first hatched and grow 1 ft a year, reaching maturity at 6 years.

The biter bitten
Young alligators fall an easy prey to carnivorous fish, birds and mammals, and at all stages of growth they are attacked and eaten

29

David Hughes

△ *A female alligator builds a nest of rotting vegetation for her clutch of 15–80 eggs. She stays for 2–3 months by the nest until they hatch.*

▽ *Alligators spend much of their time basking on the banks of jungle rivers. Here they have made a lagoon by their thrashing about.*

James R Simon: Photo Res.

by larger alligators. This natural predation was, in the past, just sufficient to keep the numbers of alligator populations steady. Then came the fashion for making women's shoes, handbags and other ornamental goods of alligator skin. So long as these articles remain in fashion and command a high price, men will be prepared to risk both the imprisonment consequent on the laws passed to protect alligators and the attacks of the alligators themselves.

There is also another commercial interest, detrimental both to the alligator and to the fashion industry. For, while the fashion for skins from larger individuals shows no sign of abating, a fashion for alligator pets also persists – though it may have dropped in intensity since its inception. Baby alligators are still being netted in large numbers for the pet shops, but – as so commonly happens with pets taken from the wild – not all those caught are eventually sold. Of a consignment of 1,000 hatchlings that reached New York City in 1967, 200 were already dead and putrefying, and many others were in a sorry condition and unlikely to survive.

In addition to persecution, land drainage has seriously affected the numbers of the American alligator. The Chinese alligator is an even worse case. Its flesh is eaten and the various parts of its body are used as charms, aphrodisiacs and for their supposed medicinal properties. The New York Zoological Park has recently announced plans to try and breed the Chinese alligator and so protect it from complete extermination.

Pets down the drain

The fashion for alligator pets has its disadvantages for owners as well as the alligator populations. Even setting aside the largest recorded lengths for the American species of 19 ft upwards, it still achieves too large a size to be convenient in the modern flat, and people who invest in an alligator often find it necessary to dispose of it. Zoos have proved unable to deal with the quantity offered them – Brookfield Zoo near Chicago has built up an enormous herd from unwanted pets – and it is widely said that unfortunate alligators are disposed of in such a way that they end up in the sewers. One result of this is that every now and then, despite official denials, reports have appeared in the press to the effect that the sewers of New York are teeming with alligators that prey on the rats and terrorise the sewermen.

class	**Reptilia**
order	**Crocodilia**
family	**Alligatoridae**
genus & species	***Alligator missisipiensis*** *American alligator*
	A. sinensis *Chinese alligator*

▷ *The hatchling alligators peep loudly and the female removes the layer of vegetation over the nest to help them escape. Baby alligators are 8 in. long when first hatched and grow 1 ft a year, reaching maturity at 6 years.*

1 cm
1/2 in.

American robin

The early colonists in America gave the name robin to a redbreasted bird that reminded them of the 'robin redbreast' of their homeland. Both American and European robins are members of the thrush family, as is betrayed by the speckled breast of the young birds, but the American robin is more closely related to the song thrush, blackbird and fieldfare than to the European robin. Indeed, the American robin was called the fieldfare by some colonists.

The American robin is the size of a blackbird. The head, back, wings and tail are a dark brown or black, with black and white speckled throat and a white ring around the eyes. The breast and belly are brick-red, much darker than the breast of the European robin.

Van Riper

American robins have 2 or 3 broods a year and feed their nestlings on insects. Building the bowl-shaped nest may be done in one day's feverish activity by the female, the male helping only by collecting material to give to her, and if she is too busy to take it he may even drop it all.

Distribution and habits

The range of the American robin covers most of the USA, as well as southern Canada. To the north, it is found breeding just beyond the tree-line, and in the south-eastern states its range is extending south-wards towards the Gulf of Mexico and the Atlantic Ocean. While the robin is more common in deciduous woodland, it is tolerant of extremes and may be found anywhere from dense forests to open plains.

The American robin is migratory, the whole population shifting south in the autumn so that the most northerly robins spend the winter where their more southerly neighbours breed. In the spring, the robins are among the first migrants to return to any area so that they are well-known as harbingers of spring; like cuckoos or swallows in England.

Although mainly a woodland bird, the American robin has achieved the same status as best-known and best-liked of wild birds as the European robin has this side of the Atlantic, because it has adapted its habits to share man's environment. They are both commonly seen searching for food on lawns and they also nest in houses and sheds, even in odd places like motor tractors.

Feeding

American robins feed on a mixture of berries and insects, no doubt turning to which-ever is most readily accessible. An exam-ination of some stomach contents showed that 42% of the diet was made up of insects; half being beetles and half grasshoppers.

Hen bird works hardest

Throughout its range the American robin is one of the first birds to begin laying. Nests are found 2–10 ft from the ground, but they may be as much as 80 ft up in trees.

Normally there are two broods; some-times three. The nest for the first is usually made in coniferous trees as the deciduous trees preferred for the second brood are bare at this time.

The nest is built by the female, with the male assisting only by collecting material. Even so, he makes fewer trips and carries less material in any trip than his industrious mate, and if she is busy shaping the nest when he arrives, he is likely to drop the lot rather than wait to give it to her.

Building the bowl-shaped nest may take as little as one day's feverish activity by the female robin. There are three stages in its construction. First the rough, outer foundations are laid down, long coarse grass, twigs, paper and feathers being woven into a cup-shaped mass. Then the bowl itself is made out of mud laid inside the main mass. If there is no readily available source of mud the robin makes her own, either by soaking a beakful of dry earth in water, or by wetting her feathers then rubbing them in earth. If there is no hurry and no egg is imminent, work will stop for a day or two to let the mud dry. Finally a

The American robin is as popular in the United States as the European robin is on the other side of the Atlantic. It was called a robin by the early colonists because its red breast reminded them of the familiar bird from 'home'. It, too, likes to live with men, searching for food on lawns and nesting in garden sheds and odd places like motor tractors. The other bird in the picture is a female Lapland Bunting or Longspur.

Joe Van Wormer: Photo Res

lining of soft grass is added.

One to six, but usually three or four, blue-green eggs are laid and are incubated for a fortnight by the female only. She continues brooding the chicks while they are very young. Later she does so only during bad weather and at night. Sometimes her mate helps feed the chicks.

Enemies

At one time the American robin was recognised as a game bird in some of the southern States. Although unlikely to have provided much sport it was no doubt as palatable as our blackbird, which once was regarded as a delicacy. Now, the robin enjoys protection over its whole range.

Cowbirds frequently parasitize American robins, laying their eggs in robins' nests in the same manner as cuckoos. Domestic cats catch adults and young, and the introduced house-sparrows, or English sparrows as they are known in America, plunder the nests.

An international feathered friend

A well-known journalist once wrote an article explaining that the friendliness of the robin redbreast was due to the bird's habit of following large animals around to feed on worms and insect grubs exposed in the earth churned up by their hoofs. For the next week he was inundated with letters from readers. Some were written more in sorrow than in anger, others were plainly abusive. The best letter, signed 'Jobbing gardener, aged 65' told, in almost poetic terms, of a robin that daily shared the gardener's midday meal, and ended with the words '. . . and you can jump into a lake'.

Something of this widespread affection for the robin must have possessed the people of Great Britain from very early times for wherever they went in the world any bird with a red breast was likely to be called a robin. The most famous is the

American robin, which is really a thrush, and that is why it is given this separate entry. In Australia several birds are called robins. They are mainly flycatchers. One of the same kind in New Zealand, with a red breast, is named 'robin'. There is an Indian robin, and the Peking robin, commonly kept as an aviary bird, is a babbler. The Jamaican tody is called 'robin', and in various places there are robin-chats, bush-robins, scrub-robins and magpie robins. These represent a diversity of birds, having little more in common than red feathers somewhere on the breast, that probably originally reminded settlers of home.

class	**Aves**
order	**Passeriformes**
family	**Muscicapidae**
genus & species	*Turdus migratorius*

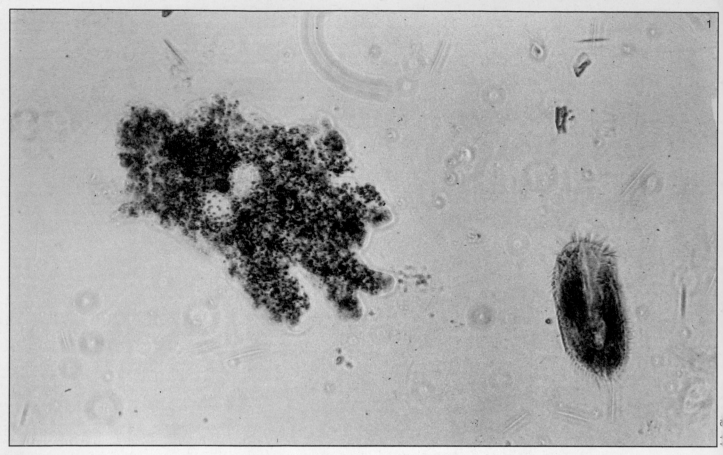

Amoeba

Amoebae form a group of the single-celled organisms called Protozoa or Protista. Protozoa means 'first animals', and as these organisms have affinities with plants (some of them photosynthesise) the term Protista — 'first creatures' — is preferred nowadays.

Like any cell the amoeba consists basically of an envelope containing the substance protoplasm. *In the middle of the cell, surrounded by the protoplasm, is the* nucleus, *a body which can be thought of as a blueprint for the organisation of the cell's activities. If an amoeba is cut in two the half with the nucleus may survive and reproduce; the other moves around for a while but cannot digest its food, and when its reserves are gone it dies.*

The protoplasm is not, as was once thought, a jelly; it has a very complicated structure, apparently consisting largely of an intricately folded and changing double-layered membrane which forms itself into a variety of minute structures which perform the cell's diverse functions.

Many amoebae

The name amoeba is applied not only to members of the genus *Amoeba* but to a range of different types of Protista with pseudopodia (see below) living in the sea, in fresh water, in damp soil and in the bodies of larger animals. They include some with shells, like *Arcella,* and also the half-dozen species that live in the human mouth and digestive system, one of which is the cause of amoebic dysentery *(Entamoeba).* Some amoebae contain many nuclei, among them the giant *Chaos chaos,* which may be six times the length of *Amoeba proteus,* measuring up to 3 mm.

Amoeba proteus, the textbook amoeba, measuring about ½ mm., is just visible to the naked eye and may be found in fairly still fresh water. It moves about by extending a finger of protoplasm, called a pseudopodium ('false foot'). As the pseudopodium enlarges, the cell contents — protoplasm and nucleus — flow into it, while the rest of the cell contracts behind. Though it has no definite shape, the amoeba is not a shapeless sac of protoplasm, for it has a permanent hind end and forms its pseudopodium in a characteristic pattern according to the species.

Feeding

The amoeba feeds mainly on other Protista. It does so by 'flowing' around them, the protoplasm completely surrounding the food to enclose it in a 'food vacuole' containing fluid in which the prey was swimming. Digestion is a similar process to that occurring in many other organisms: digestive juices are secreted into the food vacuole and the digestible parts are broken down and absorbed. The rest is merely left behind as the amoeba moves along.

This process is known as phagocytosis, from the Greek 'eating by cells'. In a similar process called pinocytosis, or 'drinking by cells', channels are formed from the cell surface, leading into the cell. Fluid is drawn into the channels and from their tips vacuoles are pinched off. The fluid is then absorbed into the protoplasm in the same way as the digested contents of the food vacuoles. This is a method of absorbing fluids in bulk into the cell.

Water is continually passing in through the cell membrane as well as being brought in by phagocytosis and pinocytosis. Excess is pumped out by contractile vacuoles which fill with water and then collapse, discharging the water to the outside.

Reproduction

The amoeba reproduces itself by dividing into two equal parts, a process known as binary fission and taking less than an hour. It begins with the amoeba becoming spherical. The nucleus divides into two, and the two halves move apart and the cell then splits down the middle.

Sometimes *Amoeba proteus* reproduces in a different manner. The nucleus divides into hundreds of small ones and each becomes surrounded by a little cytoplasm and a tough wall — all within the original cell. The resulting 'cysts' can survive if the water dries up and can be dispersed to found new populations. Larger cysts may be formed without reproduction taking place, when the whole cell surrounds itself with a thick wall. Though some amoebae reproduce sexually, *Amoeba proteus* has never been seen to do so.

Pushing or pulling?

The story of the amoeba illustrates not only the advances made in the last few decades in the techniques of microscopy but also the difficulties involved.

Years ago microscopists could watch amoeba only from above in the usual manner of looking at very small objects. From this angle one could see the pseudo-

Popular protozoan

1 *The well known one-celled animal, amoeba, showing large water excreting vacuoles. This picture includes a Stylonychian which belongs to another, ciliated, group of protozoans. (Magnified 150 times.)*
2 *Amoeboid movement — streaming of the cytoplasm can be clearly seen.*
3 *Diagram of modern microscope's side view of amoeba moving to the right on small protoplasmic pegs with pseudopodium, or false-foot, extended.*
4 *Amoeba with nucleus, which controls cell, divided, prior to cell splitting into two.*
5 *Special light phase contrast microscope gives this beautiful view of amoeba showing food in vacuoles.*

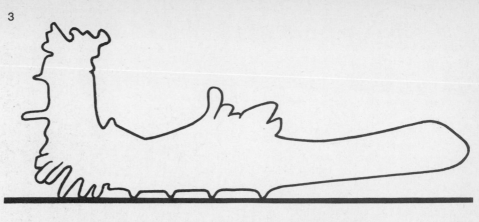

podia advancing over the surface of the microscope slide and apparently in contact with it. Recently, however, a technique has been devised for watching it from the side and a new detail has come to light. In fact, when each pseudopodium moves forward it is supported by an extremely small peg of protoplasm which remains attached to the ground at one spot while the rest of the animal, raised just above the ground, advances over it. Finally, the pseudopodium is withdrawn and reincorporated into the body of the amoeba.

A number of theories of 'amoeboid movement' have been proposed over the last 20 years but its mechanism is still not thoroughly understood. One can see, under the higher powers of the microscope, the protoplasm streaming forwards along the centre of the pseudopodium and moving out to the sides at the tip in what has been descriptively named the 'fountain zone', and there acquiring a firmer consistency. At the same time the reverse change occurs at the 'tail', where the protoplasm resumes its forward flow.

What is still in doubt is whether the advancing protoplasm is being pushed forward from behind, like toothpaste in its tube, or pulled by changes in the proteins in the fountain zone. The problem is by no means trivial, for some of our own cells move in an amoeboid manner and its solution in terms of the behaviour of protein molecules could cast light on one of the basic properties of protoplasm.

phylum	**Protozoa**
class	**Sarcodina**
order	**Lobosa**

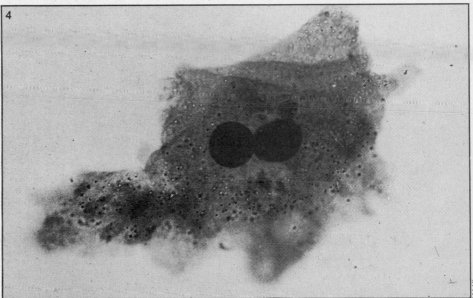

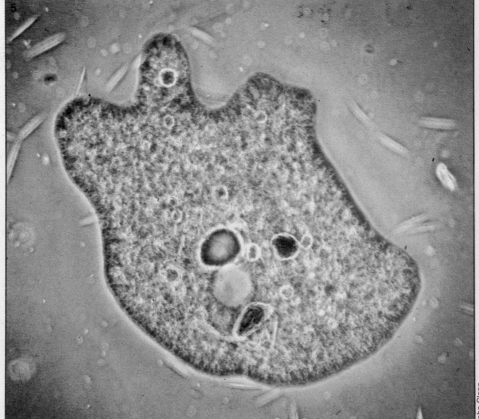

MJ Hirons

John Clegg

Amphipods

There are some animals which, either because they are small, out-of-the-way, or otherwise unfamiliar, earn no common name, yet have either an important impact on human affairs or are unusually interesting in their own right. The amphipods are a good example. They could be described as a kind of shrimp and one of the better known among them is often spoken of by naturalists as the freshwater shrimp. But it is not truly a shrimp, which is why more commonly it is referred to by its scientific name Gammarus.

Just over ½ in. long, greenish brown, its body is flattened from side to side and its back is curved in an arc when at rest. It has many pairs of legs, those on the front part of the body being used for walking, those on the hind part for swimming. This is what amphipod means (amphi—both, poda—legs; both kinds of leg). The front four pairs of legs are directed forward, the hind three pairs backwards, which is a characteristic feature of amphipods. It has two pairs of antennae and a pair of small compound eyes that are not on stalks like those of true shrimps. Its gills are at the bases of the first four pairs of legs and when Gammarus is at rest it vibrates the first three pairs of abdominal legs to drive a current of fresh water over the gills.

Over 1,000 species of amphipod are known, ranging from the near microscopic to species an inch or more in length.

World-wide 'shrimps' and hoppers

Species of *Gammarus* are found in fresh water, brackish water or in brine pools, and other amphipods live in the sea. These live in burrows in mud, inside sponges, among seaweed or swim at the surface. One species in Europe and the east coast of USA is a pest because it bores into wooden pilings. Another kind, familiar to those holidaying by the sea, lives under the piles of seaweed in the drift-line, just above high-tide mark. When the seaweed is turned over these jump in all directions, like so many fleas. They have, as a consequence, been called sandfleas, also sandhoppers and shoreskippers. They jump by using the abdomen and the last three pairs of legs as a spring. When moving about they swim on their sides, slithering over the mud using their first three pairs of legs.

Scavenging feeders

Amphipods are scavengers, feeding on any kind of dead organic matter, plant or animal, though they may attack and devour live animals smaller than themselves, which often leads to cannibalism, the larger amphipods eating the smaller.

Amongst the seaweeds and eelgrasses there live members of the family Caprellidae, or skeleton shrimps, carnivorous amphipods that lie in wait for their prey.

They are spindly creatures, with bodies as slender as a thread and the abdomen no more than a tiny stump, that creep through the weeds rather like a caterpillar. They stretch out their long front legs and hang on with the clinging feet, then draw up the posterior end and grasp the weed by hooked hindfeet.

When feeding a caprellid hangs on with its hindfeet and stretches out, remaining still until its prey bumps into it. Instantly the victim is grasped with the first two pairs of legs and devoured. This technique is rather like that of the praying mantis.

Father carries mother and babies

The freshwater shrimp (*Gammarus*) is often seen in pairs, with the slightly larger male carrying the female under his body. The female carries her eggs in a brood-pouch situated under her thorax. The young remain in this for a few days after hatching, and then a whole family may be seen swimming together, the male carrying the female, who has young ones in her brood-pouch. Sometimes the mother squeezes the sides of the pouch with her legs to force the young out. They seem reluctant to leave their shelter and hang on to the bristles on their mother's legs.

Food for everything else

Amphipods almost deserve to be called a bread-basket to aquatic carnivores. In the lakes and rivers they form the staple diet of many fishes, including trout. The sandhoppers are eaten by shore birds, one of which, the turnstone, turns over pebbles and seaweed with its bill at low-tide in its search for hoppers. It is a similar story in the sea, especially for those amphipods that swim freely at the surface, where they form part of the plankton on which many fishes, whales and some sea birds feed.

Other amphipods

Some amphipods are amphibious, and in the tropics there are amphipods living on land in the damp earth of rainforests. Some of the land-hoppers have become established in greenhouses in temperate countries, imported in the earth on the roots of tropical plants. There are others, more truly aquatic, that live in deep wells and underground springs and are known as wellshrimps.

Other amphipods have become parasitic, making their homes on other animals and feeding on their flesh. One such species is the whale louse. Like the skeleton shrimp its abdomen is a mere stump, but its body is broad and flattened from top to bottom (dorso-ventrally). The legs end in sharp hooked claws by which the whale louse anchors itself to a whale's skin. Once attached, it remains anchored in one spot for the rest of its life, eating the surrounding flesh until it is lying in a cavity. The young ones settle down close to their parents and in the end, masses, formed of thousands of whale lice, cover large patches of the skin of a whale.

A few marine amphipods use their host merely as a shelter, in which they can feed and breed with comparative ease and safety. Jellyfishes and salps provide the best homes; jellyfishes because of the edible scraps they drop while feeding, salps because of the continuous stream of water passing through their barrel-like bodies.

There is one amphipod that has taken the partnership with its host farther than the others, having developed both its anatomy and its life history to a peculiar degree. This is the sea-squirt flea, an American species that looks like a woodlouse, which lives on the body of a sea-squirt growing in sheltered parts of rock pools. Moreover, it grows on only one particular sea-squirt which must remain submerged, or at least grow in moist crevices sheltered by overhanging seaweeds. Tests in an aquarium showed that if the sea-squirt flea was put on a sponge or another kind of sea-squirt, it would wander around ceaselessly until it finally died.

The newly-emerged sea-squirt fleas crawl away from their mother on their backs, with the first four pairs of legs turned backwards to propel them. Finding a suitable crevice in the sea-squirt skin, the young flea slides into it, the middle pair of walking legs remaining turned downwards to hold on to the floor of the crevice. The other pairs of walking legs grasp the edges of the crevice and pull them together. When the sea-squirt flea grows it has to find a larger home, so it forsakes the crevice and finds another suitable spot. Still lying on its back it takes hold of the sea-squirt skin on each side and slowly pulls inwards until it has formed a cavity with the edges meeting over it.

Normally, the sea-squirt flea allows the lips of the cavity to part so that it is exposed to the water. The swimming legs beat gently to drive a current of water over its gills while the antennae are used for collecting food. The bristles that run the length of the antennae become clogged with particles and minute organisms, which are removed by wiping the antennae with the legs and passing the accumulated ball of food to the mouth.

Whale lice in a scar on the skin of a rorqual.

class	**Crustacea**		
order	**Amphipoda**		
genera	***Caprella*** *skeleton shrimp*		
	Cyamus *whale louse*		
	Gammarus *freshwater shrimp*		
	Phronima *sea-squirt flea*		

The freshwater shrimp is often seen in pairs, with the slightly larger male carrying the female under his body. Above right

There are over 1,000 species of amphipod. One of the best known is the sandhopper shown here. Right

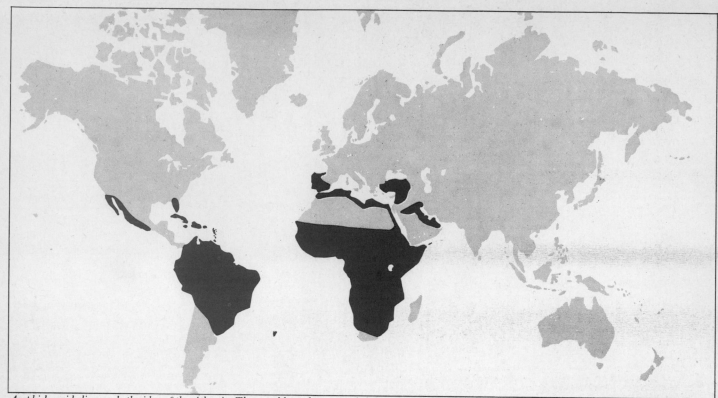

Amphisbaenids live on both sides of the Atlantic. They could not have crawled round by the land bridge which once existed across the Bering Strait nor swum across the ocean. Their distribution therefore lends weight to the theory of continental drift, which argues that the continents have slowly separated over millions of years. It is thought that America and Africa were once joined and separation began only after the amphisbaenids had evolved.

Amphisbaena

Amphisbaenids, or worm lizards, are a family of lizards of which little is known, even by zoologists, as they live underground and so cannot be observed in the wild state. There are over a hundred species, but the adaptation to a burrowing life has made them all very much alike. All external traces of limbs have been lost, except in one genus, Bipes, in which there are small, but well-developed, front limbs. The eyes are very small. The body, which is usually 1—2 ft long, is covered with scales arranged in rings, so it looks superficially like an earthworm. It varies little in general shape, except to be thicker or more slender in different species. There is more variation in the head. This may be flattened from side to side or from top to bottom, and most commonly it is blunt in front, when it tends to resemble the tail which is also blunt.

Since its eyes are so small and not easy to detect, there seems little difference between the amphisbaena's head and tail. The deception is increased by the way the animal waves its tail, when disturbed, in the same manner as a snake waves its head. The name amphisbaena is a corruption of 'amphivena' meaning 'coming both ways', for the Greek and Roman authors, and later the mediaeval monks, thought it had a head at either end of its body and believed that one head woke the other up when it was time for it to take over guarding the eggs.

Distribution and habits

Amphisbaenids live in tropical or subtropical countries on both sides of the Atlantic. In America their range extends from Argentina and Paraguay up through the Caribbean with one species in Florida. *Bipes*, the amphisbaena with front legs, is found in Lower California and along the west coast of Mexico. Others live in Africa, mainly to the south of the Sahara, but one genus extends into Turkey and Asia Minor, and into Spain and Portugal; and two other genera are found in Arabia and Socotra. Another North African amphisbaenid has a bad reputation among the local peoples, who believe it to be the young of the horned viper, which is very poisonous.

The presence of amphisbaenids in America on the one hand and Africa on the other, with none to be found in Asia or Northern Europe, shows what is called a discontinuous distribution. This could have come about in one of two ways. At one time amphisbaenids may have ranged across the world, from Africa to America via Europe and Asia. Then, because conditions became less favourable for them in Asia, they became extinct except at the two ends of their original range. Their present distribution may, however, also be explained by the theory of continental drift. According to this theory, which is becoming increasingly acceptable to scientists, all the continents were once joined, but over millions of years this one large land-mass broke up and its separate parts have slowly drifted apart. One of the telling arguments in favour of the theory of continental drift is the way the bulge of north-west Africa can be fitted into the cavity represented by the Caribbean. Bring the two continents together and it is

easy to see how amphisbaenids may once have lived in an area that was later separated, leaving one part in Africa and the other in America. Once separated, the populations in each continent would have evolved along different lines so that there are now different species in the two continents. Certain other species distributions give further evidence supporting this theory, notably arapaima and the lungfishes.

Amphisbaenids spend most of their lives underground, usually coming to the surface only at night or after heavy rain, just as earthworms do. They appear to be solitary animals, each living in its own system of burrows, which are about a foot below the surface, and they are typically to be found near streams or trees where the soil remains moist. After heavy rains fresh burrows may be dug nearer the surface. Amphisbaenids can also be found living on the surface under boulders or logs.

When travelling over the surface an amphisbaena moves very differently from other reptiles. Instead of the side-to-side serpent-like movement of other legless reptiles, it moves in a straight line hitching its body along like an earthworm. Sometimes it may move by throwing the body into vertical undulations. *Bipes* uses its pair of legs for moving the front part of its body, pulling itself along with a strange overarm movement. The American amphisbaenid *Rhineura floridanae* has been known to enter its burrow tail first; the legs folded flat against its body using the worm-like motion.

Insect eater

Insects and their larvae are the main food of amphisbaenids, which have the strong, sharp teeth needed for cracking the hard

Amphisbaena grows from 1—2 ft and its body is covered in scales arranged in rings so it looks superficially like an earthworm.

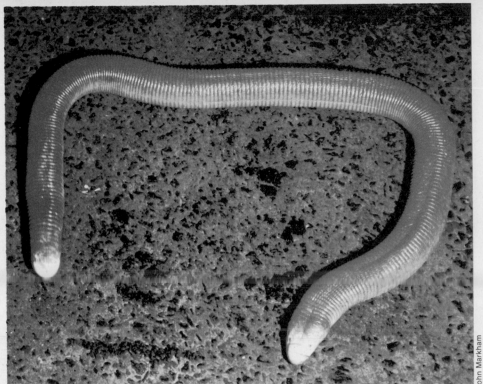

John Markham

All 100 or so species of amphisbaena, or worm lizard, look very much alike because of their adaptations to a burrowing way of life. Since the eyes are so small and difficult to detect there seems little difference between the amphisbaena's head and tail.

bodies of insects. Other soil-living invertebrates are also eaten. Some of the food supply comes from insects and other animals that might crawl into an amphisbaenid burrow to find shelter.

Many amphisbaenids live in the nests of ants and termites, where there is no shortage of food. They are immune to the attacks of their hosts, being unaffected by the bites of even the dreaded army ants. In South America the habit of living in ants' nests has led to the amphisbaenids being called 'ant-king' or 'mother-ant' by the local people, who think they are fed and reared by the ants.

Eggs laid in ants' nests

Little is known about the life history, except about the eggs and the egg-tooth. Nearly all the amphisbaenid eggs that have been found were from ants' nests. These were presumably eggs of species that habitually live in ants' nests, and to lay eggs here would have a two-fold advantage. They would be incubated in the constant, warm temperature of the nest, and the babies would have a plentiful supply of food when they emerged.

The baby amphisbaenids have a striking peculiarity which sets them apart from the young of snakes and lizards. All three have an egg-tooth, a special tooth used for tearing open the leathery eggshell. The egg-tooth of snakes and lizards is outside the mouth, on the upper lip. Soon after the snake or lizard has emerged from the egg, the tooth drops off and is not replaced. The amphisbaenid's egg-tooth, however, is inside the mouth and curves forward so that it sticks out beyond the lips, and when it drops out it is replaced by a permanent tooth.

Burrowing lizards confuse experts

Several different groups of reptiles, especially among lizards, have developed an underground burrowing way of life. In all, including amphisbaenids, similar adaptations for burrowing have been evolved. The most obvious is the reduction in size or total loss of the limbs, which would only get in the way. Alternatively the tail, which is so often thin and frail in normal lizards, has become stout and muscular, being used to force the animal along its burrow. Again, several burrowing reptiles have almost lost one of their lungs. Amphisbaena is no exception, but whereas the others have lost their left lung, it has lost the right.

To withstand the pressure when being forced through the soil, the head is more strongly built than in some of the other reptiles.

There is also a reduction in the sense organs on the head, which would be damaged by the abrasive action of soil particles. Thus, we find that burrowing animals—the mole is a good example—have inconspicuous eyes and ears. Amphisbaenids have minute eyes and these are protected by a transparent scale or 'spectacle' covering each eye. Almost useless eyes are not a disadvantage to burrowers because they live in almost perpetual darkness. The ears are also covered over, and it is likely that they are unable to hear airborne sounds, but they will doubtless pick up vibrations caused by their prey or enemies moving through the ground.

Most animals specialised for burrowing have relatives not quite so specialised and it is possible to look at these and trace the

evolution of the burrowing forms. The amphisbaenids' adaptations for a burrowing life have been so complete it is hard to say which of the other reptiles are their near relatives. All known amphisbaenids are complete burrowers. Even among the fossil forms there are no 'half-amphisbaenids' which might show relationships with other groups of reptiles. But we do have a few clues. The possession of an egg-tooth and the paired generative organs of the male at least suggest that amphisbaenids are related to snakes and lizards. Even this was once in doubt.

Side view of head of amphisbaenid

class	**Reptilia**
order	**Squamata**
suborder	**Sauria**
family	**Amphisbaenidae**
genera	*Amphisbaena*
	Bipes
	Monopeltis
	Rhineura

Amphiuma

Amphiuma, of which there are two species only, is an aberrant amphibian living in the south-eastern United States. It is characterised by a much elongated body, dark brown or black, with ridiculously short legs. The two-toed amphiuma reaches a maximum of 2½ ft in length, and the three-toed species goes up to 40 in.
It moves, both on land and in water, by lateral movements of the body.
They have three pairs of short, white external gills and their bodies are covered with small, light spots. The larvae, unlike the adults, swim by paddling with their legs. The change into adulthood takes place when they are 3 in. long.
The external gills are lost and replaced by lungs, but some larval characteristics are retained, such as one pair of gill slits. These and the lack of eyelids indicate that Amphiuma *is a primitive amphibian.*

This amphibian has been known by a variety of vernacular names, such as ditch eel, lamper eel (from a supposed resemblance to a lamprey) and blind eel. The last name refers to the vestigial eyes, which can be of little use to the animal. It is more frequently known as the Congo eel and Congo snake. These two names are of especial interest. The first springs from a belief, held in the days of the slave trade, that the animal was brought from Africa. Contrasting with this is the suggestion that it was the negroes in Florida who called it the Congo snake, believing it to be poisonous. Scientists gave it the name Amphiuma, *and this is the name which is now more often used.*

Distribution and habits

Amphiumas spend most of their time hiding in burrows beneath the water, extending their heads above the surface to breathe, and withdrawing immediately they sense any vibration. They usually emerge completely only after heavy rain, or to lay their eggs. Amphiumas can be fairly long-lived.

The two-toed amphiuma is found in rivers and streams, drainage ditches and swamps from Virginia to Florida, and westwards to Louisiana. The three-toed is found further west, from Alabama to Texas, and northwards through the states along the Mississippi to Missouri.

Amphibian cannibals

Amphiumas feed at night—when the temperature is above 17−21°C/65−70°F—on insects, smaller amphibians, fish, crayfish and small snakes, as well as a few snails and spiders. They are also reputed to feed on smaller members of their own kind. Such predatory habits are rare amongst insect-eating amphibians, although the larger frogs and toads are known to take mice. Amphiumas are aggressive when handled, being able to deliver a painful bite. It is also said that they coil their bodies round their victims at times, like some snakes.

Lays its eggs on land

Little is known of their courtship behaviour, but a sure sign that the breeding season has started is the appearance in July of adults with fresh mutilations. These are the results of adults twisting off each other's limbs during courtship antics.

Fertilisation is internal and, although mainly aquatic animals, amphiumas lay their eggs on land under logs or stones in swampy ground, between May and October. The eggs, covered in jelly like those of frogs, are laid in strings; as many as 50 by the two-toed amphiuma and 150 by the three-toed amphiuma. Each egg is ⅓ in. wide. The female protects the eggs by coiling herself around them. When they hatch she loses interest. This is not surprising since the sole value of the female coiling herself around the eggs is to prevent them drying up.

A tool for research

Amphiumas are common in south east United States and consequently they have been much used for research work, for not only must an animal have some feature of interest to scientists to be a subject for

Amphiuma is a primitive amphibian whose physiology has been studied in relation to fishes and other amphibians. It helps to show how amphibians evolved from fishes and how animals became adapted to life on land.

study, it must exist in readily available numbers. Interest in amphiumas has centred around their physiology, the workings of various organs; and their cytology, the structure and function of the different cells within those organs. Amphiumas are worthy of interest because they are primitive amphibians and their physiology and cytology can be compared with those of other amphibians, reptiles and fish. By comparing them we can find how these animals are adapted to their particular way of life, and how they evolved.

One series of experiments, for example, was concerned with the amount of water in the body. The body water can be thought of as being contained in three compartments: within the cells (intracellular water),

between the cells (extracellular water) and in the blood (this is included in the total of extracellular water).

The object of the experiments was to find the quantities of water in the three compartments.

Amphiumas were shown to have 79% of their body weight as water and of this 22% was extracellular water. As it stands this is a mere statistic, just another piece of information about amphiumas. The interest to an experimenter lay in comparing these figures with those for a toad, an amphibian like the amphiuma, but one that lives on land. It had less body water. These figures were then compared with what is known for fishes. Freshwater fishes have more body water than marine fishes. So sea and land animals have less water in their bodies than freshwater animals. This is what we ought to expect working from first principles. Both terrestrial and marine animals are faced with problems of water conservation. The latter because the high concentration of salt in sea water tends to suck water out of the body, the former because on land water evaporates into the surrounding dry air. This means, therefore, that so far as amphiuma and other freshwater

animals are concerned the problem of water conservation does not arise.

Often a piece of scientific research looks like nothing more than proving the obvious. This is because in science nothing should be taken for granted. Moreover, there is nothing more capable of misleading than 'the obvious'. It should always be viewed with suspicion.

class	**Amphibia**
order	**Caudata**
family	**Amphiumidae**
genus & species	***Amphiuma means*** 2-toed amphiuma ***A. tridactylum*** 3-toed amphiuma

Anaconda

The largest snakes are to be found in the boa family, and the largest of these is Eunectes murinus, *the anaconda or water boa. Probably no animal has been the subject of such exaggeration in respect of size. The name itself is said to come from the Tamil words* anai *for elephant and* kolra *for killer. Properly this name must have originally referred to the anaconda's relative, the Indian python. Claims for 140-ft anacondas have been made and 40 ft often occurs in travel literature. The famous explorer, Colonel Fawcett, claimed to have killed a 62-ft anaconda and was pronounced 'an utter liar' by London opinion. In fact, a 20-ft anaconda is a large specimen, although it must be presumed that larger individuals do occur. It is difficult to find an authentic record for the largest anacondas. The measurement of $37\frac{1}{2}$ ft for one specimen has been widely accepted by scientists but not by all. Long ago, the New York Zoological Society offered a prize of 5,000 dollars for a 30-ft anaconda. This has never been won.*

The anaconda is olive green with large, round black spots along the length of its body and two light longitudinal stripes on the head. It lives throughout tropical South America, east of the Andes, mainly in the Amazon and Orinoco basins, and in the Guianas. It extends north to Trinidad. The species is variable in colour and size giving rise to numerous sub-specific names. However, these can be regarded as merely geographical variations. The closely related Eunectes notaeus *of Paraguay is known as the Paraguayan or southern anaconda.*

Life by jungle streams and swamps

Water boa is a good alternative name for the anaconda, the most aquatic of the boas. It is apparently never found far from water; sluggish or still waters being preferred to rapid streams. It is this preference that limits the species to the basins east of the Andes. Swamps are a favourite haunt.

Anacondas have, as a rule, fixed hunting grounds and generally live alone, but they are occasionally seen in groups.

Largely nocturnal in habit, anacondas lie up during the day in the shallows or sunbathe on low branches, usually over water. On land they are relatively sluggish, but they are able to swim rapidly and often float motionless, allowing the current to carry them downstream.

Killing by constriction

Anacondas usually lie in wait for their prey to come down to the water's edge to drink, whereupon they strike quickly with the head, grabbing the luckless prey and dragging it underwater so that it drowns. At other times anacondas may actively hunt prey on land.

The usual prey caught by lying in wait are birds and small mammals—deer, peccaries

Anaconda is the largest of snakes, reaching up to 37 ft, although exaggerated claims give lengths of 140 ft. They kill their prey by constricting. Each time the victim breathes out, the anaconda tightens its coils until the animal dies of suffocation.

and large rodents such as agoutis. Fish also form a large part of the diet, a fact not surprising in so aquatic an animal. More surprisingly, turtles and caimans are sometimes attacked. There is a record of a 25-ft anaconda killing a 6-ft caiman. The special jaw attachment that snakes have allows an anaconda to swallow such a large victim. After a meal of this size, which will suffice an anaconda for several weeks, the snake rests for a week or more until digestion has taken place. Normally the diet will consist of more frequent smaller meals.

Most snakes are adapted for swallowing prey wider than themselves: the upper and lower jaws are only loosely attached, and the brain protected from pressure by massive bones. Also a valve on the breathing tube allows the snake to breathe while swallowing.

The method of killing the prey is the same as in other constricting snakes such as the pythons. The prey is not crushed, but merely contained; each time the victim exhales, the coils of the anaconda tighten around its chest so that the ribs cannot expand, thus preventing inhalation until it suffocates. Stories in travelogues refer to anacondas' prey having every bone in the body broken and being squashed to pulp. In reality, bones are rarely broken during the process just described, which is one of strangulation. The fallacy is due to confusion between freshly-killed and regurgitated prey. This is covered with mucus, which gave rise to the story that anacondas

41

smear their prey with saliva to facilitate swallowing.

Breeding

Few observations have been made on the breeding cycle of the anaconda. Males of southern anacondas studied in captivity were apparently aroused by the scent of the females. The male moves up alongside the female, flicking his tongue over her, until his head is resting over her neck. When in this position, he erects his spurs, two claw-like projections which are the last visible remnants of the hind limbs. The spurs are moved backwards and forwards against the female's skin and when the cloacal regions are in opposition, a hemipenis is inserted and copulation takes place.

Anacondas, like other boas, are viviparous. From 20—40, sometimes up to 100 young are born in the early part of the year. Each baby is 2—3 ft long.

Anacondas in folklore

It is not surprising that such a large, and malevolent-looking creature should be the subject of folklore and fallacy. The South American Indians have numerous stories about the anaconda, from the belief that it turns itself into a boat with white sails at night, to the mythology of the Taruma Indians who claimed to be descended from an anaconda. Several factors have led to tales of giant snakes. For one thing size is notoriously difficult to estimate unless a comparison can be made with something of known dimensions. Exaggeration is more likely if the animal is moving and writhing around, or if the observer has had a shock, as he might well have on suddenly seeing an anaconda. Secondly, snake skins stretch very easily when being prepared so that the length of a skin gives no concrete evidence. It is not therefore difficult to see how stories of giant snakes could have arisen, and, once started, how this has led to unwitting or deliberate embroidery. Along with stories of venomous qualities and body size, there is exaggeration about the danger involved in meeting an anaconda. This is not unique; all large carnivorous animals become surrounded by stories of their man-eating habits. Many accounts are pure fiction. Only a few years ago a book was published describing a 140-ft anaconda, and how the author narrowly escaped from a 45-ft specimen by shooting its head off.

Other stories are reported truthfully but are not evidence of man-eating habits, but of self-defence, for when man blunders into an animal it is not surprising that it tries to defend itself. There are, however, remarkably few authentic stories of people killed and eaten. Rolf Blomberg, who has made many searches for record-sized specimens, has been able to find only two fairly definite instances of anacondas killing human beings. In only one case was it claimed that the victim, a 13-year-old boy, was eaten. Even this was somewhat doubtful because the story goes that he disappeared while bathing with friends. On discovering his absence, one of them dived down to search and saw an anaconda. The victim's father then hunted down the snake and shot it. Blomberg states that the boy's body had

Zool Soc London

△ An alternative name for the anaconda is water boa as it is never found far from the sluggish forest streams or swamps. They move relatively slowly on land but can swim rapidly and often float motionless, allowing the current to carry them downstream.

▽ Anacondas often lie up during the day in branches over the water's edge and wait for their prey to come down at night to drink, when they strike quickly with the head, grab the prey in their coils, often dragging it down into the water, to drown.

Russ Kinne: Photo Res

been vomited up but does not say whether, in fact, it was recovered or whether this was only surmise. In the other incident a grown man was captured by an anaconda while swimming and was drowned. His body, when later found, had distinct marks of having been subjected to a powerful squeeze, but there was no indication of his having been swallowed.

Here then are two reports of the death of human beings, caused by anacondas. As we have seen, there is some doubt about one of them and in the second the man may have been killed but there is nothing to show he was eaten. In fact, few anacondas would be large enough to swallow a man. Nevertheless, such stories, perhaps in a garbled form, would travel through the country, so giving the impression that anacondas are man-

eaters. After this, anyone who disappeared and was last seen at the water's edge would be presumed to have been eaten by the anaconda, especially if one of these large snakes was seen in the vicinity. Such stories are so sensational that nobody asks for details or unequivocal evidence and the travellers would then take home a supposedly authentic story to relate to eager and uncritical audiences. So the anaconda is branded and its man-eating habits become part of folklore.

class	**Reptilia**
order	**Serpentes**
family	**Boidae**
genus	*Eunectes murinus*
& species	*E. notaeus*

Anchovy

The name of several out of nearly 100 species related to herrings. Members of the anchovy family are similar to herrings, except that they are mainly smaller, their maximum size being 8 in.

The anchovy familiar to Europeans is the small fish (Engraulis encrasicholus) that is canned or converted to anchovy paste. To Americans the anchovy is a very similar fish, of a different species, the northern anchovy (Engraulis mordax), ranging from British Columbia to Lower California, used in quantities as live-bait. A similar fish, called anchoveta (Cetengraulis mysticetus), represents for the Peruvians a sea-harvest that brought about an economic revolution. Anchovies elsewhere in the world are also fished commercially.

Vast shoals

Anchovies are most abundant in tropical seas but large numbers also live in the shallow parts of temperate seas, in bays and estuaries. Some species live even in brackish or fresh waters. They are one of the most numerous, if not the most numerous of marine fishes, the herring not excluded, and like the herring, they live in large shoals. Within the smaller shoals the large individuals tend to be below, the smaller individuals above, so light is allowed to filter through the whole shoal. This is probably important for shoaling behaviour. It has been noted in aquaria that a fish will swim towards another of similar size and appearance but of a different species, then sheer away when about a foot from it, as if it had discovered its mistake.

With larger shoals the formation is somewhat different. The anchovies separate out in sizes, and it is believed that the larger individuals drive away the smaller, which shoal on their own. This characteristic shoaling behaviour of the anchovy makes it especially valuable for canning—the catch does not need to be sorted out for size.

Plankton feeders

Like the herring, the anchovy is a plankton-feeder. But whereas herrings will select certain animals in the plankton, picking them up one at a time, the anchovy swims forward with its mouth open, taking in small plankton more or less indiscriminately.

The behaviour of the shoals is determined by the feeding method. If a shoal of anchovies swam straight forward those in front would capture the food, those in the rear would go hungry. Instead, the leading individuals turn to either side and return to the rear of the shoal. So each gets its turn to feed. One result of this is that the shoal assumes the shape of a tear-drop. When plankton is dense, however, the leading individuals fan out and the shoal assumes an oval shape, with its long axis at right angles to the line of advance.

The depth at which the shoals swim depends on the movements of plankton, which migrates to the surface by day and sinks down again at night.

Breeding

The shoals of adult European anchovies frequent the Bay of Biscay and the Mediterranean but migrate through the English Channel in spring to spawn. Their spawning ground was the Zuyder Zee, until this was reclaimed. Now it is the Elbe estuary. The eggs are oval and float at the surface, hatching 2—4 days after fertilisation.

Reaction to enemies

The main enemy is the tunny. The reaction of the anchovies to its presence is to clump. A shoal may be spread out, several hundreds across. At the approach of a tunny the shoal contracts to form a living, writhing sphere, of thousands of fishes, a few feet across. Those with the least well developed shoaling instinct, which remain on the fringes of

layers of guano. Thousands of tons of this rich fertiliser were gathered every year, such a rich harvest that the birds responsible were protected by government. Furthermore, great shoals of these small fishes were caught to supply the fish markets.

In the early 1950's it was argued that birds must digest 20 tons of anchovetas to produce 1 ton of guano. The same amount of fish could be machine-ground to produce 4 tons of fish-meal. Blended with soya-bean meal it could be exported for pig and poultry feed. As a result a new fishing industry sprang up. Since 1955 the populations of Peru's ports have been quadrupled by people moving in to work there, a fleet of 1 500 fishing boats is at work, and Peru exports annually fish products worth $137 000 000 (£57 000 000).

▽ *Of the 7 million tons of fish harvested by Peru each year, much consists of these tiny fish whose maximum size is only 8 in. Anchovies are typified by a rounded snout and small jaw set far back.*

▽▽ *Thousands of anchovies make a shoal which keeps together by hearing water rushing over their bodies. A well spread out shoal will suddenly contract into a writhing sphere of fish when threatened.*

the frightened group, will be eaten by the tunny. Laboratory tests suggest that in any shoal there are a few individuals that panic less readily than the rest. In an alarm situation these 'stand their ground' and the rest congregate around them. The anchovies detect tunny by the sound of the larger fish moving through the water.

Profitable new industry

Most fisheries have a history stretching back into the distant past, but one important fishery is less than two decades old. The plankton-rich Humboldt Current supports multitudes of fish, mainly silvery anchovetas 3—6 in. long. These have been the food of sea-birds that rest on the islands off the coast, whose cliffs became covered with deep

To conserve this harvest a Marine Resources Institute has been established at Callao. At present there is no indication of the supply of fish giving out although in 1964 Peru harvested 7,000,000 tons of fish, much of it anchovetas. Meanwhile, the sea-birds that once produced the guano eldorado are in poor shape, perhaps because so much of their food is being taken from them.

class	**Pisces**
order	**Clupeiformes**
family	**Engraulidae**
genus	*Cetengraulis mysticetus*
& species	*Engraulis encrasicholus*
	E. mordax
	and others

Anemone

'Anemone', from the Greek for wind, was first used for a flower in 1551. At first the marine animals that look like flowers were called plant-animals. The name 'sea-anemone' was not used until 1773. Today, marine zoologists almost invariably speak of the animals as anemones. That they are truly animals is no longer in doubt although the order to which they were assigned is still called the Anthozoa, that is, plant-animals. The basic differences between plants and animals are:

1 A plant manufactures its own food, by photosynthesis, using the green chlorophyll in its leaves; an animal takes solid food.

2 A plant is incapable of locomotion; an animal can move about.

3 A plant has no obvious sensitivity; an animal usually has recognisable sense-organs.

There are exceptions to all three principles, especially among the lower plants and the lower animals, but these are good working guides.

A sea-anemone has simple sense-organs, takes solid food and, surprisingly, is capable of locomotion.

The most outstanding feature of sea-anemones is the variety of their colours and, in many species, the beauty of the patterns these make. Colours and patterns in higher animals are known to serve as camouflage, warning coloration, recognition marks and other utilitarian purposes. Sea-anemones neither need nor could use any of these; their colours and patterns consequently appear as pure art-form.

Long-lived and motile

Anemones are found only in the seas but there they are world-wide, from between tide-marks to the great depths of the ocean. They are most abundant in warm seas where they can reach up to 3 ft across. The smallest are little more than a pin's head, but this requires some explanation. Voracious feeders, anemones will eat any animal flesh they can catch and swallow, and they may swallow prey of large size relative to their own bulk. It is not unknown for one anemone to swallow another and they are not immune to each other's poison. They can, however, survive for a long time without food, gradually dwindling in size until quite minute. This may be one of the secrets of their long life—anemones have been kept in aquaria for as much as 100 years.

Sea-anemones are by no means 'rooted to the spot'. There are even burrowing anemones. Those that are normally seen fixed to a rock move by gliding on their base. Others somersault, bending over to take hold of the substratum with their tentacles, then letting go by the base and flipping this over to take hold beyond. A few species lie on their side to glide along, or blow themselves up, let go with their foot, and float away.

Stinging tentacle feeders

An anemone is a cylindrical bag with a ring

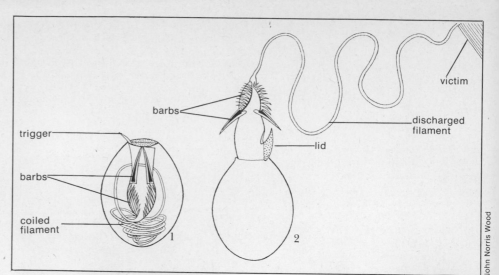

John Norris Wood

Jane Burton: Photo Res

Fatal flowers
of the sea

Left 1. Bag-like stinging cell of coelenterate full of paralysing poison and with coiled filament inside.

Left 2. When the cell is activated by having its trigger touched or by food chemicals, the lid flies open and the coiled contents turn inside out, shooting the poison-filled filament into the body of its victim, which is also retained by the barbs.

ES Hobson

△ Anthopleura xanthogrammica, *the giant green anemone, is one of the few anemones to live in direct sunlight. Its green colour is due to a minute one-celled green alga living in its cells and photosynthesising.*

ES Hobson

△ *Anemones can have little use for warning coloration or camouflage, so their colours appear as nature's art. This red anemone is* Taelia crassicornis.

▽ *Plumose anemone,* Metridium senile, *can be quite large, up to 9 in. high and 6 in. across the head.*

Dramatic picture of life in tropical seas. ▷

◁ *Triggered by the touch of an unfortunate fish the anemone's tentacles, with their barbed and paralysing stinging cells, wrap around it and carry it to the mouth.*

Helmut Stellrecht

45

of tentacles surrounding the mouth on the upper surface. The opposite end is flattened and forms a basal disc, or foot, by which the animal sticks to a solid support. The interior of the bag is one large stomach, subdivided by curtains of tissue, or mesenteries, which hang down, partially dividing the stomach into eight compartments. Food is caught by the tentacles, which are armed with stinging cells. When a small animal, such as a shrimp or a fish, touches a tentacle the stinging cells come into action, paralysing and holding it. Adjacent tentacles also bend over to continue the stinging and holding until all begin to move towards the mouth, where the prey is engulfed. Indigestible remains from a meal are later voided through the mouth.

Stinging cells are a characteristic of the phylum Coelenterata to which sea-anemones belong, and included in the phylum are jellyfishes, the stinging cells of which are more familiar to most people. The Coelenterata are accordingly spoken of as stinging animals or, better still, nettle animals. Sting-cells, or nematocysts, are double-walled capsules, filled with poison, set in the outer surface of the tentacles. Each contains a coiled hollow thread, sometimes barbed at the base. At the outer end of the capsule is a thorn-like trigger. When this is touched the coiled thread is shot out. It turns inside-

and contraction of these muscles the body can be drawn out or pulled in. There is also a series of retractor muscles which assist in the sudden withdrawal of body and tentacles. There are only very simple sense-organs and there is only a simple nerve system, a mere network of nerve-cells.

The action of the nematocysts is automatic, the result of the trigger being touched—it is a reflex action. A nerve strand also runs to the base of each nematocyst and it is these nerve strands that control the concerted action of the tentacles once a nematocyst has been discharged. The nerve network comes into action to cause the contraction of an anemone when it is touched. It can be made to expand again by adding a nutrient solution to the water. The slime from a mussel, for example, in the proportions of one part in a million, will make the body expand, and the tentacles extend, very slowly, perhaps taking an hour to come full out. Then the body sways slightly and the tentacles wave as if groping for food.

Sexual and asexual reproduction

Most anemones are either male or female, but some are hermaphrodite. In some, eggs and sperm are shed into the surrounding water, in others the larvae develop inside the parent body. The eggs vary in size, the largest, only 1 mm wide, being a thousand

arise from the base of a parent, become separated and move away. Laceration occurs in some species with a roving disposition. As the anemone glides over the rocks pieces of the base are ripped away and, being left behind, regenerate to form very minute but otherwise perfect anemones.

Enemies

Enemies are large sea-slugs, sea-spiders, fishes and sometimes starfishes and crabs.

Restless anemones

Aside from their diverse methods of locomotion, which are used but sparingly, anemones are always on the move, in a kind of slow-motion ballet. This led to an important discovery, the subject of which was the plumose anemone, 3—4 in. high, with a feathery crown of numerous small tentacles. When several scores of these are living in a large aquarium they are seen, at any given moment, to be in different attitudes. The body of some may be stretched up, others shortened and thickened; perhaps it is shortened and slender, its surface thrown into wrinkles, or it may be bent over to one side. The tentacles also will be in various stages of extension and retraction. Sometimes one or more anemones will be dilated and their tentacles withdrawn, so that they look like balloons anchored to the rock. Others may be so withdrawn that they look like buttons on the rock. They may be watched for some minutes and no movement seen; but when anemones are watched closely and continuously against a black background, and their shapes drawn at intervals, they can be seen to be in continuous movement. This has been confirmed by other experimental methods, including a speeded-up film. Even when anemones are kept under conditions of constant temperature, in water free of food or undisturbed by vibrations the rhythm of activity continues. It can be interrupted by the presence of food or other disturbing factors, when the anemones react by more purposeful movements. One effect of this inherent rhythm of activity is to keep the animal in a state of constant preparedness for feeding, defence and other activities essential to the maintenance of life.

This movement is called the inherent rhythm of activity because it is self-starting and self-maintaining. It is common to all living organisms, as we now know. Obvious manifestations of it are seen in such processes as the beating of the heart, as well as in less obvious ways. When we sleep, for example, we do not simply lie still. Our bodies are in constant, if slow movement, in much the same way as the bodies of plumose anemones were shown to be.

Jane Burton: Photo Res

Newly budded babies around beadlet anemone, Actinea equina, *after asexual reproduction.*

out as it is ejected, its fine point pierces the skin of the prey, and the paralysing poison flows down the hollow thread. Some kinds of nematocysts stick to the prey instead of piercing the skin, and in a third type the thread wraps itself around the victim. In addition to being triggered off by touch some nematocysts come into action in the presence of certain chemicals.

The body-wall of an anemone is made up of two layers of cells. There is, however, a good series of muscles. One set is longitudinal, running from the foot to the bases of the tentacles. The other is circular, running round the body. By the lengthening

times larger than the smallest. The fertilised eggs sink to the bottom and divide, or segment, to form oval larvae. These move about the seabed but finally each comes to rest, fastens itself to the bottom, grows tentacles and begins to feed.

An anemone can reproduce in other ways. It may split longitudinally to form separate individuals, or grow a ring of tentacles half-way down the body, after which the top half breaks away to give two anemones where there was one before. Young anemones may be formed, in some species, by fragmentation, or laceration. In fragmentation small anemones, complete with tentacles,

phylum	**Coelenterata**
class	**Anthozoa**
order	**Actinaria**
genera	*Actinea*
	Anemonia
	Metridium
	and others

Marine angelfish, Angelichthys, living among the coral reefs of tropical seas, outstanding for its varied patterns and colours.

Angelfish

The name 'angelfish' has been used commonly for three types of fishes. The first is a relative of sharks, which we treat under its alternative name, monk-fish. The other two are bony fishes, one of which is marine, the other freshwater. The latter has long been a favourite with aquarists who, perhaps to avoid confusion of names, developed the habit of using its scientific name, Scalare. *Since not every-one followed their example, however, at least part of the confusion remains. There is another perplexing usage. Some of the fishes belonging to the same family as the marine angelfishes are called butterfly fishes, but the butterfly fish is only dis-tantly related to these and belongs to an entirely separate family.*

There is little to chose between these angelfishes and butterfly fishes. The one distinguishing mark is the spine on each gill-cover in angelfishes, which is lacking in the butterfly fishes.

It hardly needs explaining that these vernacular names are prompted by the enlarged flap-like or wing-like fins.

Most angelfish are small, up to 8 in. long, but some reach 2 ft in length. The outline of the body, because of the well-developed fins, has much the shape of a flint arrowhead. The name of one of them, 'spadefish', conveys a similar idea of shape.

Colourful and curious

The marine angelfishes, and the related butterfly fishes, which together number more than 150 species, live mainly in shallow seas and a few enter estuaries. They live in pairs or small groups at most, around reefs, rocks or corals.

They are inoffensive as adults except for the forceps fish of the Indo-Pacific. This is highly aggressive, erecting the spines of the front part of the back-fin and turning its body at an angle to rake the flanks of another fish. Not only are other angelfish peaceable, they do not dash away as most fishes do when, for example, a skin diver intrudes into their living space. They move away but slowly, every now and then tilting the body to take a closer look at the newcomer.

The forceps fish is also unusual in using its long snout at the surface to send out small jets of water. It does not have either the skill or the force used by the archerfish and the purpose of this waterspewing is unknown.

The outstanding feature of these fishes is the wide range and the beauty of their colours and patterns. In many of them the young fishes have the same colours as the adults, but in others the differences are so great that it looks as if there are two dif-ferent species involved. Their behaviour tends to be different also. Quite small —that is, up to a few inches long—they tend to be solitary, and individuals are usually found in the same places day after day, in each case near a shelter into which the fish darts when disturbed. The shelter may be under a rock bed or among seaweed. A tin can lying on the sea-bed will readily be used for shelter. In an aquarium the sub-adults will be aggressive towards each other, but one kept on its own readily becomes tame and learns to feed from the hand.

Probably the most beautiful of the angels is the rock beauty, coloured jet black in front and yellow in its rear half, its fins bright yellow with red spots. It has a strong sense of curiosity that makes it draw near to the underwater swimmer. The queen angelfish, when small, is largely dark brown to black with three bluish vertical bands on the sides of the body and a bluish band along the dorsal fin. Adult, it is mainly a startlingly bright yellow with irregular and diffuse patches of violet or red on various parts of the body. The French angel is black with strongly contrasting bright yellow vertical bands and a yellow face.

Feeding

Angelfishes have small mouths armed with many small teeth and they use these to crush the small invertebrates on which they feed. In some species the snout is somewhat elongate, and is inserted in cracks and crevices in rocks or coral to capture small animals for food.

Parental care

Little is known of the breeding habits of marine angelfish, but they probably conform to the pattern of their better known rela-tions in that they show quite close care of the eggs and fry.

Both fish clean a patch of flat rock, and the female lays her eggs on it, the male swimming close over them shedding sperm for fertilisation. The eggs are tended for 4—8 days by the parents, when the fry hatch, and sink to the bottom.

The parents guard them until they are sufficiently free-swimming to hide in crevices and weed. The fry are unlike the adults in that their bodies are long and slim. They do not assume full adult shape before three or four months have passed.

Popperfoto

△ *Angelfish are strongly territorial and use their colours both to advertise possession of their territory and to warn off an intruder of their own species. One of these freshwater Scalare is displaying at the other with a sideways flick of its bright pectoral fins like flashing signals.*
▽ *These freshwater angelfish, Scalare, are favourites with aquarists.*

▷ *Marine French angelfish, Pomacanthus paru, showing one of the bizarre shapes and patterns typical of these fish, which look quite different from the side than the front view.*

Stephen Dalton

Jane Burton : Photo Res

Wasted artistry?

All angelfishes and butterfly fishes are conspicuous. To the underwater swimmer their colours stand out and 'hit the eye'. Especially striking are the patterns of the imperial angelfish or blue angelfish, with their inscribed patterns of white and black curves and half circles on a rich blue and violet background, dazzling to the eye when seen at close quarters.

We are used to the idea of colours and colour-patterns serving as camouflage to hide an animal from its enemies or enable it, if a predatory animal, to steal close to its prey undetected. We are used also to conspicuous colours, especially combinations of yellow, black and red, serving as warning colours, the wearer of these colours being poisonous or bad-tasting or having a sting. The colours of angelfishes certainly fail to hide their wearer. Although one writer has described angelfishes as nestling among coral heads like hummingbirds among brilliant blossoms, most underwater swimmers agree you can see these fishes clearly at a distance. There is no indication that angelfishes are poisonous or unpalatable, or have a sting. They are eaten by the local peoples wherever they occur, although their skins are said to be tough.

Perhaps the comparison with hummingbirds is not so far-fetched as it appears at first sight. Conspicuous colours in birds are associated with displays, especially aggressive displays, as they are in lizards such as the anole and the same may be true of angelfishes. Experimentally, a mirror was placed in an aquarium with a French angelfish. The fish drew near, nibbled at its reflection in the mirror, then threw itself sideways and flicked its bright blue pectoral fins like flashing signals. This suggests that angelfishes are strongly territorial and use their colours both to advertise possession of a territory as well as to warn off an intruder of their own species.

There was at least one angelfish that escaped attention for a long time despite its colouring, a bright orange head with a glowing dark blue contrasting body. This, the pygmy angelfish, was wholly unknown until 1908, when one was brought up in the trawl off Bermuda from a depth of 540 ft. It was dead when it reached the surface and its carcase was committed to a jar of alcohol to preserve it. It became something of a mystery fish and it was not until 1951 that it was given a scientific name, when one scientist examining it realized it was a new species of angelfish. The next year a second specimen was taken from the stomach of a larger fish, a snapper, caught in 240 ft of water off Mexico. In 1958, this fish, believed to be so rare, was caught in fair numbers by a skin-diver off the Bahamas, in 40 ft of water. Widespread in American tropical seas, living at various depths, and evidently very elusive, this small angelfish had no colloquial name until 1959—when it was dubbed 'cherubfish'!

class	**Pisces**
order	**Perciformes**
family	**Chaetodontidae**

51

Anglerfishes

There are more than 350 species of anglerfish, the Pediculati, but because of the distinct differences between them it is convenient to consider them as two groups: anglerfishes (225 + species) and deep-sea anglers (125 species). All have developed the characteristic habits of anglers: they keep still most of the time, using a rod and line to catch small fishes. The rod of the anglerfish is a modified spiny ray of the dorsal fin. Habitual immobility means little expenditure of energy, and less need for breathing. This is reflected in the small gills of anglerfishes with only a small gill-opening.

'Pediculati', the old name for anglerfishes, means 'small foot', referring to the elbowed pectoral fins used like feet to move over the seabed in short jumps. The pelvic fins are also somewhat foot-like but they are small, usually hidden on the undersurface in advance of the pectoral fins. Because of their squat shape, bottom-living habits and method of locomotion the anglerfishes have been given a variety of descriptive vernacular names: goosefishes, monkfishes, frogfishes or fishing frogs (because of the wide mouth) and batfishes. One of the best-known is Lophius piscatorius, *up to 4 ft long with a large head, about 2½ ft across, and a wide mouth. Although the fish is so ugly the flesh is highly palatable and is widely used as fried fish.*

Camouflaged and immobile

Anglerfishes of one kind or another are found at all depths throughout tropical and temperate seas. Bottom-living for the most part, their bodies are ornamented with a variety of warts and irregularities, as well as small flaps of skin. These, with their usually drab colours arranged in a broken pattern, serve to camouflage the fish as it lies immobile among rocks and seaweed. The sargassum angler specializes more than most anglerfishes in camouflage. It lives exclusively among the weed of the Sargasso Sea, and uses its pectoral fins to grasp the weed, so that it is not easily shaken from its position.

Angling for food

The general method of feeding is to attract small fishes near the mouth with some form of lure. In the goosefishes and monkfishes this is a 'fishing rod' bearing a fleshy flap at its tip, which is waved slowly back and forth near the mouth. In others the rod lies hidden, folded back in a groove, or lying in a tube, and is periodically raised or pushed out and waved two or three times before being withdrawn. The lure at the end of the rod often is red and worm-like in shape. A small fish seeing it swims near and then suddenly disappears!

Breeding

Four deep-sea species of anglerfish show a peculiar relationship between male and female; the dwarf male, about ½ in. long, attaches itself to the female (whose length is up to 45 in.) so securely that the two grow together, even sharing a blood system. The female is then, in effect, a self-fertilising hermaphrodite, the male being reduced to a mere sperm-producing organ.

Another outstanding feature of the breeding cycle of some anglerfishes is the size of the egg-masses. The female goosefish or frogfish lays eggs in a jelly-like mass, up to 40 ft long and 2 ft in width. This floats at the surface. The relatively large pear-shaped eggs are attached by the narrow end to a sheet of spawn, which floats at the surface, and may contain nearly 1½ million of them.

The larva, even before it leaves the egg, begins to develop black pigment. Seen from above the spawn appears as a dark patch in the water, the enclosed larvae looking like currants in a cake. One of these masses, seen by rowers in a boat off Scapa Flow, was mistaken for a sea-monster and the rowers pulled away from it for dear life! The larva is in an advanced stage when hatched and already has the beginnings of its fishing rod. Later, other spines develop on the back and branched fins grow down from the throat, so the larva looks very unusual.

The Compleat Angler

It is an interesting pastime to list how many human inventions have been anticipated in the animal kingdom. Anglerfishes have used a rod and line (or a lure) long before man did. It is not surprising that both human and fish anglers should use similar methods because their aims are identical. But although attention is always drawn to this, by writers on the subject, nobody seems to have commented on the other piece of apparatus the two have in common: the landing net. Both kinds of anglers play their fish but the anglerfish does not allow his quarry to take the bait. Instead, the lure is waved until a fish draws near, then it is lowered towards the mouth. As the victim closes in on it the rod and its lure is suddenly whipped away, the huge mouth is opened wide, water rushes into this capacious 'landing net' and the prey is sucked in, after which the mouth snaps shut.

Anglerfish's body is camouflaged by flaps of skin resembling surrounding seaweeds.

And it all takes place in a flash. Only when a fish is large, so that the tail protrudes from the mouth after the first bite, can we see what has happened. The anglerfish's ability to snap up its prey like lightning is quite remarkable. One moment the small fish is there near its mouth, the next moment it is no longer there, and the speed with which the anglerfish moves its jaws is too fast for the human eye to follow.

The batfishes take their angling to even greater lengths. The whiskery batfish, of the Caribbean, for example, is covered with outgrowths of skin that look exactly like small seaweeds and polyps known as seafire, that coat rocks like so much moss. Small fishes are deceived to the point where they will swim near and try to nibble the flaps of skin. The final touch to this masterpiece of deception lies in the batfish habit of gently rocking its body, making the

Small fishes attracted to the anglerfish's mouth by a lure are snapped up. (⅓ natural size.)

flaps of skin sway from side to side, just as polyps and seaweed gently sway as the slow currents in the sea move back and forth. This is so much an ingrained habit that a batfish, removed from its surroundings and placed in an aquarium, will periodically rock itself even although it is surrounded only by clear water and glass.

When the small fish, deceived in this way, swims near, out comes the rod with its lure, looking like a wriggling worm. With this the batfish 'plays' its quarry. It will dangle the lure in front of the fish then withdraw it to entice the little fish nearer. It will vary the wriggling of the lure, now waggling it in an agitated manner, now moving it slowly. Watching this one gets the impression of a fish 'playing cat-and-mouse' with a smaller fish until—'snap'—and only the larger fish can be seen, motionless, and with a dead-pan expression.

class	**Pisces**		
order	**Lophiiformes**		
families	**Lophiidae** *anglerfishes*		
	Antennariidae *frogfishes*		
	Ogcocephalidae *batfishes*		

Angwantibo

A rare member of the family Lorisidae, to which the lorises, pottos and bush-babies also belong. The angwantibo is frequently confused with the potto, but it is smaller, with a head and body of 10 in., and has a longer muzzle and smaller eyes placed closer together. The limbs are proportionately long, while the tail is a mere stub hidden in the fur. This gives the angwantibo a rather spider-like appearance. The ears are naked and the hands and feet only sparsely covered.

There are two subspecies. One has yellowish-brown or fawn fur with whitish underparts and the other, somewhat smaller in size, is generally golden-red above with greyish underparts. In both the fur is thick and wool-like with a golden sheen that is reponsible for their alternative name of golden potto.

Angwantibo is probably derived from 'Angwan', the common West African word for cat.

Habits

The angwantibo was unknown to Europeans until 1860, when it was discovered in the Cameroons. Since then only a few have been collected. They are restricted to an area lying between the Niger and Congo rivers. Angwantibos live in the tall trees of the tropical deciduous forests, but are sometimes found in the secondary forests that spring up where the original trees have been cut down.

Little is known of the angwantibo's habits as they are nocturnal. However, they are occasionally seen out in broad daylight. It is not known whether this is unusual or whether, like other animals, such as foxes and mice, they are thought of as being only nocturnal, yet habitually come out at some time during the day. What little is known about their habits has been learnt by collectors and by observations on specimens in zoos. Gerald Durrell, who collected three specimens, found that they were most active at dawn and dusk. When asleep their arms are put between the legs so that the front feet are gripping the branch behind the hindfeet and the head rests on the chest. Durrell's angwantibos always chose branches that sloped and clung to these in an upright position. On the other hand, another

The angwantibo has feet like living callipers, each capable of a vice-like grip. This is the secret of its gymnastics.

Zool Soc London

collector, Ivan Sanderson, found that his specimens, while adopting the same position as Durrell's, hung upside down from the branch. Sanderson also found that although a sleeping angwantibo could easily be awakened, its limbs could be pinched and prodded without disturbing it. This led Sanderson to think that the angwantibo had an automatic locking device in its limbs so that it could hang effortlessly in this sleeping position.

Unlike its relative the potto, the angwantibo is very active and agile, nimbly weaving its way through the dense foliage of the forests. This agility is demonstrated by its method of changing direction while walking upside down under a branch. It stops and thrusts its head back between its legs. The front legs change direction and follow the head until it is poking out from between the hind legs. Now it swaps its hind feet round so that the body is straightened out, but all its limbs are going up above its back while it is hanging face downwards. So it finally swaps its hands and feet round, rolls into its original inverted position and sets off in its new direction. This seemingly complicated manoeuvre is accomplished very rapidly.

Angwantibos are unusually silent animals although they have been heard to utter a soft, hardly audible hiss when handled and a soft rather cat-like growl when afraid.

Fruit and insect feeder

There is no record of angwantibos' natural food, but in captivity they will take banana, avocado and various wild fruits. Soft-bodied insects and grubs, such as caterpillars and beetle larvae, are also favoured, but beetles and other hard-bodied insects are merely licked and set aside, although angwantibos have sharp teeth and jaws strong enough to crush them.

After each meal an angwantibo cleans itself thoroughly, combing its fur with the lower front teeth. The ears, face and upper part of the chest that cannot be reached by this method are finished off with the hands which are first dampened with saliva, rather like a cat licking itself.

Breeding

One baby is born at a time. At birth it is less than 1½ in. in length, with little fur. For the first day its eyes remain shut, then they open into slits and do not become round for a few weeks. By this time the fur is growing thicker.

At first the baby clings to the mother's belly, but later will ride pick-a-back. The mother sometimes leaves it clinging upside down to a branch.

Living callipers

The first published account of the angwantibo contained a mixture of anatomical details and local knowledge, and was somewhat worthless. Not until 73 years later, in 1932, do we find it mentioned again. Then, in 1948, one was sent to the London Zoo where it lived for only a short while. Animals as rare as this tend to be regarded as curiosities, deservedly so in this instance, and the greatest peculiarity of the angwantibo is its feet, which are living callipers,

△ *Baby angwantibo clings to the mother's back.*
◁ *Here the mother, with baby clinging to her belly, is making a complicated turn; the hind legs and back part of the body are facing the camera while the front half is turned away.*
▽ *Angwantibos have the large eyes typical of nocturnal mammals.*

each capable of a vice-like grip. This is the secret of its gymnastics.

The angwantibo's extremities have almost a nightmare quality. The hands and feet of all amphibians, reptiles, birds and mammals are based on one pattern, the pentadactyl, or five-fingered hand. The basic pattern can be seen in frogs and lizards, and from this there have been many adaptations, culminating in the wings of birds. In the primate order, to which we belong, there has been a trend towards the development of grasping hands and feet, and this is linked with the habit of living in trees. Monkeys, apes, lemurs and lorises are all tree-living and they have opposable thumbs for gripping branches. But the angwantibo has hands and feet even further developed for gripping.

The palms of the hands are naked, though the backs are hairy. The thumb is much larger than the rest of the fingers, to which it is strongly opposed. The first or index finger is reduced to a mere tubercle, and the remaining three fingers, of which the middle is the longest, are invested at the base in a common skin. In addition, at the base of the thumb is a thorny, fleshy pad, giving the appearance almost of an extra digit. The general effect of this unusual combination of digits is very similar to the foot of a parrot or a chameleon, and gives a very strong grip.

The foot is stronger and larger than the hand, but there is again the division into two opposing portions. On the one side is the large and well-developed big toe (or thumb) and this also has a fleshy tubercle at its base. The remaining four toes are well-developed and are also joined in a common skin at their bases.

For those who delight in worrying at zoological problems—without hope of solving them—it is worth while concenrating attention on the hands and feet of the angwantibo. The first thing we note is that its skeleton offers nothing peculiar, except in the bones of the hands and feet. The bones of the body are relatively straightforward. It is only in the bones of the hands and feet that major changes have taken place. Similar changes to those that ended in the human hand have gone much further, to a monstrous degree, in fact.

class	**Mammalia**
order	**Primates**
family	**Lorisidae**
genus & species	*Arctocebus calabarensis*

The pictures on these pages of angwantibos happily playing among the branches of their den in the London Zoo's modern mammal house clearly show their active and nimble movements. This agility is due to their remarkable hands and feet. The thumb and big toe are well-developed and oppose the other digits which are enclosed in a common skin at the base. The two parts of each foot can thus grip branches like living callipers.

Ani

Although unfamiliar by name, the anis are among the most unusual birds in the world; almost everything they do is out of the ordinary. The four species form a subfamily of the cuckoos, but, unlike the true cuckoo, they do not lay their eggs in the nests of other birds. Jay-sized (about 15 in. long) with black shiny plumage and long, nearly square-ended wings and long laterally-compressed beaks, they range from the southern borders of the United States to the Argentine, including many of the larger islands of the West Indies, living in brush or the adjacent open country. They are outstandingly sociable, each flock behaving like a tightly-knit clan.

Habits

The flocks usually number 7–15 and often contain a surplus of males. While flying around, the birds keep together like a flock of sheep following closely behind a leader, and uttering high-pitched cries.

Each flock holds a communal territory and defends it against neighbouring flocks. Normally an ani does not leave this territory even if chased by a man, but should it do so and then intrude the territory of another flock it will be chased out. Within a flock, however, there is little quarrelling and members will preen each other, a sure sign of sociability. If one is hurt the others will crowd around it, as if protecting it—one of the few examples in the animal kingdom of what is called compassionate behaviour.

The size of the territory depends on the size of the flock, about 10 acres for a large flock being typical. It is divided into two parts, one including bushy trees with thick foliage where the anis sleep and nest, the other open savannah where they feed.

Feeding

Although they will also take fruit, berries and other vegetation, especially in the dry season, anis are mainly insect-eaters. Much of their time is spent walking around together searching through the low vegetation of the savannah country for insects. Strangely, they make no use of their communal activities to find food. For example, other birds that forage in flocks watch specially for prey flushed from its hiding place by other members of the flock. This is the more remarkable because anis will follow other animals to prey on insects they disturb. They follow the processions of army ants to feed on the insects and other animals fleeing from the ants. Anis also hunt for winged termites, waiting on a branch then flying out to catch one and returning to the perch to eat it, like flycatchers.

They will also follow cattle for the insects disturbed by their hooves. Counts have been made of the amounts of insects a single ani can catch in a given time. In the dry season it may get three times as much food by following a cow than by hunting on its own. In the wet season, when so much more food is available, there is not such a great difference. Another advantage, in

Greater ani, Crotophaga major *spends much of its time walking around on the ground looking for insects. It often follows cattle to eat the insects disturbed by their feet. ($\frac{1}{3}$ natural size.)*

△ *Communal nest of ani with eggs of different shapes, evidently laid by two females. Rough nest is lined with fresh leaves.*
▽ *Nestling ani, about 6 days old, its feathers just beginning to unsheathe.*

the dry season, of following cattle is that the birds not only get more food but they have to walk about less to find it, so effecting a considerable saving in energy. This habit recalls that of the cattle egret and the tick bird. Anis do not, however, perch on cattle to get a free ride, as do the tick birds of Africa, and only rarely will they pick ticks and other parasites off the cattle.

Communal breeding

Nesting starts soon after the rainy season has begun. This allows the anis to change their diet from mainly vegetation to small animals ranging from insects to lizards.

One species, the smooth-billed ani, is sometimes polygamous, and this includes both polygyny, one male to two or more females, and polyandry, one female with two or more males. Even more unusual is the communal nesting and care of the young.

Occasionally a pair will build a nest on their own, but usually several pairs combine to build a single nest. Then each will work independently, with the male concentrating on bringing material to the female, who works it into position. The nest is built from leaves and twigs plucked off neighbouring trees, and is sited in a fork of a thickly foliaged tree, or in a bamboo. When finished, it is an untidy cup, usually 1 ft in diameter and 6 in. deep.

Each female lays 4–7 eggs and as many as 26 have been found in one nest. All the parents co-operate in brooding the eggs, which take 13 days to hatch. If the nest is destroyed a new one is very rapidly built and more eggs laid. With so many eggs in one nest they are piled in layers and those in the bottom do not get incubated and so fail to hatch.

The young hatch in an advanced state and can climb out of the nest after five days. If danger threatens, they scramble away across the tree using their feet and bills. The chicks are fed by any of the adults and even when they can fly they still remain in the territory and help defend it. There may be three broods raised in a year and the older chicks help their parents feed the younger ones. Some of the chicks remain with their parents and breed with them in following years.

Huddling for warmth

Each evening a flock of anis will congregate on the branch of a tree to sleep. They fluff out their feathers and huddle together in a row. This behaviour suggests that their temperature regulation is not very good and that they are liable to get chilled at night, especially as the next morning they fly out to a perch in the sun and sit there with wings outstretched.

class	**Aves**
order	**Cuculiformes**
family	**Cuculidae**
genera	***Crotophaga*** *and others*

Anole

There are 165 species in the genus Anolis, that is, one quarter of the total number of species in the iguana family of lizards. Unfortunately for the scientist, the anoles show little variety in form and so are difficult to identify. Their heads are triangular with elongated jaws. The body is slender, ending in a long, whip-like tail. The toes have sharp claws as well as adhesive pads, in the form of grooves on one of the joints, that enable the anoles to climb sheer walls. Males have a flat throat sac which can be extended by muscular action when they are excited. This expands the folds of skin to reveal a remarkable pattern of colours between the scales—green, red, white, yellow and black in many combinations.

Anoles are small lizards ranging in total length from 5 in. to the 18 in. knight anole of Cuba. Of this, two thirds is tail, so that the knight anole is by no means a large lizard. It is, however, a handsome animal, pale green with white markings on the body; on the head there is a braided pattern in yellow with patches of blue around the eyes. The male's throat sac is pale pink.

The best-known anole is the green anole from the southeast of the United States. This is a medium-sized lizard 6—7 in. long, with a beautiful pale green body marked with brown spots, the throat sac being spotted with red and white. The leaf-nosed anole of Brazil is so-called from the peculiar sideways flattened structure that projects beyond its snout for a distance equal to the length of the head.

Habits and colour change

Anoles are found only in the Americas where they range from North Carolina to southern Brazil and are abundant in the West Indies. Most of them live in trees, running around the branches with the aid of their long delicate toes and adhesive pads. A few species have enlarged toe pads which give some parachute effect, enabling the anoles to descend from considerable heights with safety. Other anoles have become associated with man, living in houses and gardens where they can take advantage of fruit in the gardens and insects that infest houses. Such anoles become very tame and some disturbance is necessary to send them scurrying. In this way they resemble the agamas and geckos of the Old World.

One of the more unusual anoles, the water anole of Cuba, lives along the banks of streams, diving into the water and hiding under stones when frightened. Also living in Cuba are two cave-dwelling anoles. One of these, a pale, translucent lizard with brick-red stripes running across the body, lives in limestone caves frequented by bats.

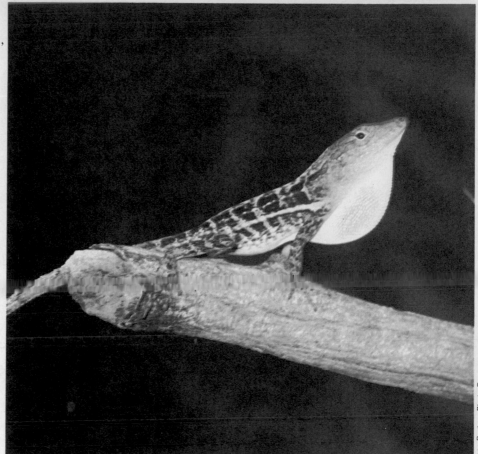

Jane Burton: Photo Res.

△ Male Jamaican anole. The long, specialised toes enable it to climb sheer walls.

▽ Anoles asleep on poinsettia. To escape, a lizard will often forfeit its tail as seen here.

Jane Burton: Photo Res.

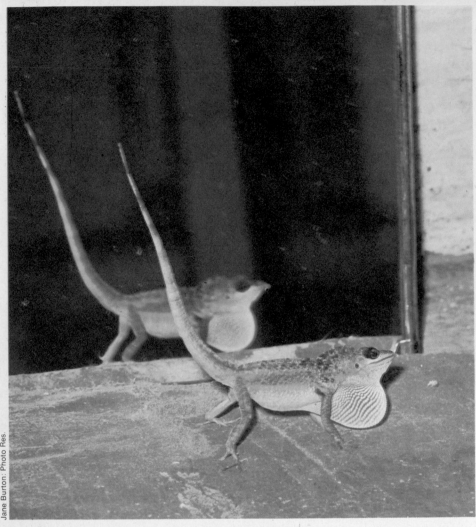

Jane Burton: Photo Res.

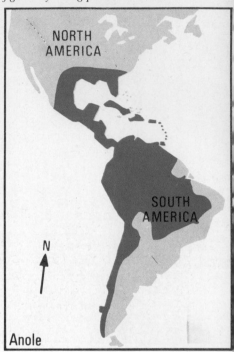

◁ *A mirror placed in this anole's territory caused regular displays by the lizard at its own reflection, as it thought the image was an intruder. Displays often lasted 3 hours completely exhausting the lizard. This anole is at the climax of an aggressive display.*

▷ *Male anole in aggressive display, showing the throat sac fully extended by muscular action to reveal the throat colours. The anole raises itself off the ground at the same time wagging its tail up and down. Display is the usual form of aggression, fights only taking place as last resort.*

NORTH
AMERICA

SOUTH
AMERICA

N

Anole

It can be found clinging to the walls of the caves in the twilight zone near the entrances, and, unlike most cave dwellers, it will come out into broad daylight.

The green anole is commonly called the 'American chameleon' because, excluding the cave dwellers, most anoles are adept at changing colour. This ability is often exaggerated and the anoles are sometimes said to be able to alter their colour and blend completely with their background, turning green when placed on a leaf and dark brown when moved to a tree trunk. Experiments and observations in natural conditions show that the anoles change colour in response to temperature, light intensity and emotional state. Background colour will affect the colour of an anole to some extent, but if it is kept cool, at about 10°C/50°F it will go brown whatever the background. If the temperature is raised to 21°C/70°F it turns green, but only so long as the light is dim. If the light is bright it stays brown. Then, if the temperature is raised another 30 or 40 Fahrenheit degrees the lizard becomes pale green and stays that colour whatever light there is. In normal conditions the green anole tends to be green at night and brown by day.

The mechanism of colour change varies in different kinds of reptiles. The pigment-containing cells in the skin, responsible for colour changes, are controlled by nerves in chameleons, so chameleons can change colour quite rapidly. In anoles, on the other hand, the cells are controlled by a hormone, a chemical messenger called intermedin which is secreted into the blood by the pituitary gland, which lies at the underside of the brain. It is carried by the blood stream to the colour cells where it causes them to alter the concentrations of pigment within. This is a slow process compared with the action of the nervous system, and anoles will take up to 10 minutes to change colour.

The pituitary gland, which controls colour change, is close to that part of the brain responsible for emotions, so it is not surprising that the colour of males is influenced by their aggressiveness. The green anole male becomes bright green if he wins a fight but brown if he loses.

Fruit and insect eaters

Anoles are fruit and insect eaters, taking whichever is available, according to the time of year.

Breeding behaviour

The male anole is larger and more brightly coloured than the female. He holds a territory which he defends against other males by displaying the colours of his throat sac and, at times, by fighting. Apart from territorial fights, there is also a peck-order system (so called as such a system of hierarchies was first studied in flocks of hens) in which the big males bully the medium ones, who in turn worry the small ones. Such encounters are short-lived, as the in-

ferior male knows his place and retreats immediately. When two equals meet, perhaps on the boundary of their territories, the outcome is more spectacular, although in the end perhaps less decisive. The two sidle round each other with bodies puffed up, then one, followed by the other, raises its body off the ground and stretches out its brilliant throat sac. At the same time the tail wags up and down. After holding this pose for a few minutes they subside and start parading again. Many bouts of displaying may take place before the two lose interest in each other and wander away, having decided nothing. Only rarely will a fight break out, the contestants grappling with their jaws and thrashing around until one breaks away and retreats at speed. The displaying and such contests as there are constitute threat and a test of strength rather than actual combat.

The throat sac is also used to attract the female, who if willing coyly turns her head to one side. The male approaches her from the rear, grabs her neck with his jaws, puts one hind foot over her body to clasp her leg, slips his tail under hers and mates. It is not uncommon in animal life that an action which a male interprets as threatening behaviour and to which he responds aggressively, will to a female indicate courtship so she will respond submissively.

The eggs are nearly always laid in the ground, the female coming down the tree to dig a hole with her snout. The eggs are

Jane Burton: Photo Res.

laid into the hole, or pushed in if they miss, and the hole is filled in. The cave anoles have a different habit. They lay their eggs in the caves, where they may be found in narrow crevices in the walls or between stalactites in groups of two to seven. As anoles regularly lay only one or two eggs at a time, it is likely that the clusters of eggs are laid by several females.

The eggs, which are not guarded, hatch after 6–10 weeks when the ground appears to swarm with baby anoles.

Many enemies

Hawks, cats, mongooses, and many other predators take their toll of anoles. In one experiment 200 were marked and released. A year later four had survived and they had gone in another 6 months. Like many abundant animals, there is a very rapid turnover of population, very few even reaching maturity although the maximum age an anole can reach if protected in a vivarium is over 6 years.

Aggression in a mirror

The territorial instinct is as strong in the male lizard as in any other animal and much of his time is devoted to making threatening displays at other males encroaching on his pitch.

A few years ago, in a house in Barbados where an anole had taken up residence, a mirror was propped against the wall to see how the lizard might react to his own image. Three days later he was seen in front of the mirror displaying at his image. He continued to do this for 1¼ hours, and after this he returned almost daily to the mirror to display at the supposed rival. Between these displays the lizard would parade backwards and forwards in front of the mirror with much animation, or would try to bite his image. Several times he went behind the mirror as if looking for his opponent.

Some of these displays would last for as much as 3 hours on end, by which time the lizard seemed completely exhausted. It was almost as if once he had stationed himself in front of the mirror he was unable to tear himself away, as if, fascinated by his own image, he was under a spell that could only be broken when somebody went into the room and disturbed him. Then he would go out to the back door, rest on the step, occasionally blowing out his throat at lizards on a pawpaw tree nearby or on a wall across the yard. Usually he would return to the mirror within an hour, but sometimes, after an initial bout of aggressive display, he would go away and stay away all day.

By the end of 6 weeks the lizard still seemed attracted by his own reflection. He had stopped actively displaying in front of it although he still paraded up and down and occasionally tried to bite his own image, and at very long intervals would display by blowing out his throat, but no more.

This was an artificial situation for the lizard and in a natural state he would not display for so long at a time, nor so vigorously because either he or his opponent would drive the other away. The importance of the experiment lies in this: while the image in the mirror represented for him another male intruding on his territory there was every indication that the lizard remembered this 'other male' and this supposed rival was seldom 'far from his mind'. For example, the lizard might be in another part of the house or on the back step, feeding or sunning himself, when he would suddenly drop everything he was doing, make a bee-line for the room in which the mirror was standing, go straight across to it and start to display. This is important in helping us to interpret one aspect, which will be discussed under crow, of the behaviour of birds that bang themselves against windows. It was not merely a case that the lizard on seeing his own image in the mirror treated it as a rival male. Again and again, he behaved as if he had suddenly remembered that in the other room was a rival demanding his attention.

class	**Reptilia**
order	**Sauria**
family	**Iguanidae**
genus & species	*Anolis* spp.

Antarctic cod

The family of fish known as the Noto-theniidae or Antarctic cod is so unfamiliar that its members are hardly mentioned in encyclopedias on fish. Yet the family, together with its relatives the Antarctic dragon fishes (Bathydraconidae) and the ice fishes (Chaenichthydae) includes 55 of 66 species of fish known in the Southern Ocean that surrounds Antarctica.

The Antarctic cod looks rather like a bullhead or miller's thumb and it takes the place in Antarctica of the bullhead family (Cottidae) of northern seas. It has a large, rounded head with a small body flattened from side to side. As the fish ages the head grows out of proportion to the rest of the body and large specimens look quite grotesque. The colouring is dark brown or black, perhaps with lighter patches on the sides, and lighter on the undersides. Two fins run the length of back and belly, the one on the back having a small fin placed just in front of it. The pectoral or breast fins are large.

Life beneath the ice

About 15 of the 30 species of Antarctic cod live in Antarctic waters where the sea temperature drops to −1·8°C/29·8°F in winter and rises to no more than a few degrees above freezing in summer. They avoid the fatal freezing touch of pack ice by living at the bottom of the sea. Usually they are found inshore in waters of less than 100 fathoms depth.

As their shape rather suggests, Antarctic cod are sluggish fish. They live among seaweed where their sombre colouring makes them inconspicuous, and they seldom go out on to the open sea bed. They do not move in shoals, but as they seek out patches of weed, quite large groups of them may gather together.

Antarctic scavengers

Antarctic cod will eat most available food. Their main items of food are crustaceans such as the isopods and amphipods abundant around Antarctic shores. Near research stations in the Antarctic, fish have been caught with potato peelings and cabbage leaves in their stomachs.

Normally the Antarctic cod merely lies in wait in a clump of seaweed and engulfs any creature that swims past, but it will sometimes shoot out to capture its prey, and one species, *Notothenia rossi*, is generally more active, swimming in mid water in chase of krill and other crustaceans.

Large yolky eggs

Each female lays 12,000−34,000 eggs. This is a very small number when compared with the 6 million laid by a single cod, but each yolky egg is large, about ⅛ in. in diameter. This is a feature of marine animals both in the Antarctic and the Arctic seas. They lay fewer and larger eggs than their counterparts in temperate or tropical waters; the nearer the poles a species lives the larger

Fishing for Antarctic cod through a hole cut in the sea ice.

and more yolky are its eggs.

Antarctic cod first breed when they are about 14 in. long, at about 9 or 10 years old. In an egg-bearing female the ripe ovary may be a quarter of the total body weight.

In May eggs and sperm are shed into the water for fertilisation to take place. This is just at the beginning of the Antarctic winter, but the temperature of the sea does not vary significantly through the year so the breeding season is probably related to the bloom of plankton in spring. Whether breeding takes place after the bloom, so the parents have had adequate food supplies to build up the yolky eggs, or whether the significance lies in the eggs hatching well before the next bloom, so it coincides with a critical stage in the development of the young, is not known.

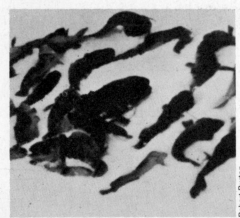
All these Antarctic cod were caught in good fishing conditions in 10 minutes.

The fertilised eggs remain near the seabed, but the newly-hatched larvae swim to the surface waters to feed on plankton. While at the surface they are silvery which, no doubt, aids in camouflage, making the fish less visible to predators above and below by reflecting the shade of the surrounding water (the reflecting mechanism of fish scales and its protective value will be discussed under Smelt). When the young fish have grown to 3½ in. they return to the bottom of the sea where they take on the adult colouring and begin to develop the characteristic large head.

Enemies—seals and shags

The bottom-living fish of the Antarctic coasts are preyed on by seals, especially Weddell and leopard seals, and also by shags which hunt in flocks. They swim round in a compact group called a raft, occasionally putting their necks under water to look for prey, then all dive at once when food has been spotted.

Instant fishing

The name Antarctic cod was given to the Nototheniid fishes not because they look like cod, for they look quite different from this silvery, streamlined fish, but because they resemble it in taste. For many years explorers and whalers have used the Antarctic cod to supplement their often dull, tinned diet. It is unfortunate that the largest part of the fish is its head and that only two thin strips of flesh can be cut off the sides of the body.

Considerable ingenuity has gone into the problem of catching Antarctic cod. Tests have been made on the best bait. Silver lures and pieces of red bunting have been tried, but the acknowledged favourite has been fresh seal or penguin meat, scraps of which are usually to hand from carcases killed for consumption by men and dogs. Traps on the lobster pot principle have been built but these are not satisfactory because the swarms of amphipods usually beat the fish to the bait. Enthusiasm for trapping finally wanes when the pots are torn away or squashed by a lump of ice.

The most popular and successful method of polar fishing is that of the Eskimo. The fisherman squats by a hole, laboriously cut through thick ice, and lowers the line to the bottom. Success depends on the position of the hole. If it is over a weed-bed fish are caught almost at once and continuously. As many as 70 can be caught in half an hour by this method. As soon as the hook is lowered a fish grabs it and, so rapidly is the bait taken, it seems as if the fish are queueing up to be caught. The moment the fish is lifted out and placed on the ice its body freezes and becomes rigid.

Sometimes fish are caught by unconventional methods. On one occasion a group of men standing by a hole in the ice were startled when a seal suddenly popped out with a 60-lb fish in its mouth. However, they were less startled than the seal and snatched the fish from its jaws.

class	**Pisces**
order	**Perciformes**
family	**Nototheniidae**
genus & species	***Notothenia*** spp.

Distribution of the Antarctic cod, family Nototheniidae. They live at the bottom of the sea to avoid the fatal freezing touch of the pack ice where the temperature is below 0°C.

Antbird

There are 221 species of antbird, arranged in 53 genera. Very few have English common names and not many have been studied in any detail in life, most of them being known only from skins brought back by collectors. Nevertheless, even the little that is known is of intense interest, and it is clear that one day a fascinating story will be unfolded. This is foreshadowed by the variety of names used. The name 'antbird' is used for the family as a whole and also, more specifically, for certain genera in that family. In addition, many members of the family have been given names with the prefix 'ant' followed by the names of unrelated birds which they resemble in some particular. Thus there are antthrushes, antshrikes, antcreepers, antvireos and several others. To make the matter more complicated, some antbirds have been given names relating to their appearance or habits, such as bare-eye, fire-eye and bush-bird. The reasons for this can be seen when we consider them in detail.

Antbirds are all fairly small, ranging from the 3½in. Antwren to the 14in. Antpittas. Their beaks are usually hooked, strongly so in the antshrikes. The plumage is generally dull but often enlivened with patches of black and white, and in many species there is a marked difference between the sexes, with the black parts of the male's plumage being replaced by brown or chestnut in the female. The male of the black antwren is almost wholly black, with only a few spots of white on its wings and, on the flanks, white patches which are exposed during display. In contrast, the female is olive grey. This sexual dimorphism, as it is called, is not found in the ant-thrushes and antpittas.

Habits and distribution

Antbirds are found on the mainland of Central and South America from southern Mexico through Central America to the northern half of South America, and also on Trinidad and Tobago. They live in thickets and forests on lowlands and on mountain ranges, but never in open country or plains.

Antbirds are very vocal, and some of them are best recognised by their song, which is often very shrill. The ant-thrush has a mellow, resonant whistle that has been described as wistful or melancholy. It is usually uttered three times but may be repeated up to ten times.

As would be expected of birds living in dense cover, they are not strong fliers. Their wings are short and rounded, and they do not migrate. With so many species occupying a relatively small region every part of it is exploited. The black-faced ant-thrush is ground-living and escapes danger by

Antbird species found in dense forests of Central and South America show a great deal of variation in size, colour and markings.

◁ *The pygmy antwren,* Myrmotherula brachyura, *lives among low, thick shrubs, feeding on snails and insect larvae (¾ of life size).*

▽ *The white-plumed antbird,* Pithys albifrons, *wanders through the forest undergrowth in flocks of 20–30, closely following columns of army ants (approx natural size).*

▽ *Wing-banded antpitta,* Myrmornis torquata, *from deep forests, spends most of its time on the ground, searching for food.*

Malcolm McGregor

Over 200 species of antbird range through the thickets and forests of lowland and mountainous areas. They never live in open plains.

Male barred antshrike, Thamnophilus doliatus, *feeding young with large insect. Despite their apparent helplessness at this stage, the young leave the nest after only 10 days. The adult resembles a true shrike in its black and white plumage.*

The plumage of the female antshrike is duller than the male's. The hooked bill helps to catch reptiles and large insects.

running, taking off only as a last resort. The antpittas also live on the forest floor. Both types have long legs and they stalk around twitching tails so short that the birds look as if they are newly-fledged chicks. The spotted antbird lives just above the forest floor and is rarely seen more than 6 ft from the ground. Antvireos and antwrens tend more toward tree life. The black antwren is found in the middle layers of the forest, never on the ground or up in the topmost branches. The barred antshrike is the best known of the antbirds because, while most of the others avoid crossing open ground, this antshrike leaves the forest to live in bushes around human settlements. Another antshrike, the black-crested, lives in mangrove swamps, coffee plantations, and on waste ground.

Most antbirds are solitary or go about in pairs, but the white-faced antcatcher is nearly always seen in tight groups and the black antwren goes around in mixed flocks of other species such as vireos, cotingas, woodcreepers and other antbirds.

Feeding—searching and following

The name 'antbird' tends to be misleading. Antbirds do not habitually feed on ants. The ant-thrushes and antpittas flick through the leaf litter with their bills looking for snails and beetles. Some of the larger species occasionally eat small reptiles and may take

the eggs and young of other birds. The black antwren forages for insects hiding in the bark of twigs. But some do live up to their name by following columns of army ants to feed off the insects and other animals that flee from these voracious hordes, although the ants themselves are not molested.

Breeding behaviour

In many antbirds, all we know of their breeding is what their eggs look like. The habits of one, however, are known better. The spotted antbird breeds in the first two months of the rainy season. The nest is built near the ground by both adults, each bird arranging its own material in the nest. If one of a pair arrives while its mate is sitting on the nest arranging material, the new arrival will wait its turn rather than hand over the material to the other.

It is not uncommon among birds for the male to feed his mate during courtship or while she is on the nest. An antbird does this and also preens her and will even do so outside the breeding season, when the pair are foraging near a column of army ants.

Two eggs are laid and are brooded by both parents, taking turns of 1—2 hours, except at night when only the female sits. After 2 weeks blind, naked, black-skinned chicks hatch out but in only 10 days they are ready to leave the nest. The rufous-necked ant-thrushes are unique among

antbirds in making nests in holes in trees, while one of the antpittas is thought to nest in epiphytic plants growing on trees well above ground.

Variations on a theme

The names of the antbirds reflect the many different habitats that members of the family have adopted. Within the deep forests they have taken up various niches, or specialised habitats, otherwise occupied by their namesakes. The antvireos have short bills and search leaves and twigs for insects as do real vireos. They also build vireo-like nests in the forks of branches. The antshrikes have well-developed hooks on their bills and take large insects and small reptiles in the same way as shrikes, which they also resemble in the black and white plumage. Elsewhere, the relationships between antbird and namesake are more obscure. Ant-thrushes resemble thrushes only in plumage, perhaps slightly in being good songsters, and antwrens are merely the smallest of antbirds.

class	**Aves**
order	**Passeriformes**
family	**Formicariidae**
genera & species	*Formicarius* spp. *Myrmotherula* spp. and others

Anteater

With its long cylindrical snout, bushy tail and inturned front feet, the giant anteater, one of three species of anteater, must be one of the most unusual-looking animals. The length of head and body is 3—4 ft and the tail another 2—3 ft.

The hair is coarse and stiff, grey-brown on the head and body, becoming darker on the hindquarters and tail. Across the shoulders are wedge-shaped black stripes bordered with white—a surprisingly effective camouflage.

The silky or two-toed anteater and the tamandua are a little less bizarre in appearance, perhaps because they have shorter snouts and no plume of long hair on the tail. The silky anteater is so called because of its soft silky coat. It is the size of a squirrel, the head and body being about 6 in. long. The prehensile tail is a little longer than this. The tamandua also has a prehensile tail, which is naked for most of its length. The fur is usually tan with a black 'waistcoat'.

Anteaters are completely toothless and are grouped in the order Edentata, which means 'without teeth'. This is a rather misleading name because the other members of the order, the sloths and armadillos, do have some teeth. Teeth are often absent in animals that live on soft-bodied insects, such as termites. Aardwolves (see p 4) are hyaenas that have taken to eating termites and have few teeth, most of which are small and weak, in contrast with true hyaenas.

Distribution and habits

Anteaters live in Central and South America. The giant anteater is found in swamps, open forests and savannahs, from British Honduras and Guatemala to northern Argentina. Both the silky anteater and the tamandua live in forests from southern Mexico to Bolivia and Brazil.

The giant anteater lives on the ground, shuffling about with its nose to the ground in an almost continual search for food. It has apparently no permanent resting place or burrow but curls up, with its head between the forelegs and tail wrapped round the body, in any sheltered place, sometimes taking over the abandoned burrow of another animal. In remote parts giant anteaters are diurnal, but have become largely nocturnal near towns.

There are two remarkable features of the anteater's anatomy: their feet and their teeth. Giant anteaters walk on the knuckles of their front feet, giving them a strange, crippled appearance. This stance appears to be an adaptation to protect the long, sickle-shaped claws from being blunted. The awkwardness of the front feet is emphasised by the nearly human shape of the hind feet. The heel rests on the ground and the five

Tamandua clinging to a branch with its strong claws. Its tongue fully extended measures 10 in. so ants can be obtained from ants' nests ($\times \frac{1}{4}$).

Okapia

toes are of almost equal length. The feet of the silky anteater are similar, but there is an extra 'joint' in the hind feet which enables the toes to be bent back right under the soles to give a good grip on branches.

Little is known about the habits of the tamandua and silky anteater. They are nocturnal, spending the day curled up in a hollow tree or on a branch.

Sticky tongue eater
Anteaters feed almost exclusively on termites, ants and soft-bodied grubs. With the sharp claws of the front feet they tear holes in the tough walls of termite nests. The long muzzle is pushed in and the 8—10 in. tongue probes around the galleries of the nest to trap the insects with its sticky saliva.

Secretive breeding
Anteaters are solitary animals, and when two are seen together it is most likely that they are a mother and her single offspring. In Paraguay, at least, the young are born in the spring, but this knowledge is based on only one report. Gestation takes 190 days and the baby clings to its mother's back until almost half her size, staying with her until she is pregnant again.

The silky anteater is reported to make a nest of dry leaves in a hollow tree and to leave her baby there while she goes out

Silky anteater moving through Brazilian forest, its long prehensile tail gripping a branch.

feeding. She is also said to feed her baby on a regurgitated mush of insects. If this is correct it is most unusual behaviour for a mammal. Feeding young by regurgitation is common among birds, but is rare in mammals where the young are fed on their mother's milk until they can take solid food.

Formidable adversary
The main predators of the silky anteater are the harpy eagle, the spectacled owl and various eagle-hawks. Its defence is to rear up on its hind legs and to slash and pinch with the long claws of the front feet, as does the tamandua. It is also said that the silky anteater seeks out the silk-cotton tree where the sheen of its fur makes it very hard to see amongst the mass of silverish fibres that cover the seed pods. The giant anteater is a formidable animal, deterring jaguars and other carnivores with its claws.

△ *Giant anteater carrying young, striding out across a South American open plain. The young will ride on her back until a year old.*

▷ *Mother tamandua,* Tamandua tetra-dactyla, *with her offspring clinging jockey style to her back.*

A nose for food

To anyone who has seen a living anteater it would seem obvious that it has a good sense of smell. The mere size of the nose, compared with the small eyes and ears, suggests that it must rely a good deal on scent. Its habit of wandering around with its nose close to the ground, probing nooks and crannies, would confirm this. Yet this is not real proof of the anteater's sensitivity to smell. The long snout could merely be a means of probing far into holes to extract insects.

On page 40, where experiments on the body water of Amphiuma were described, it was pointed out that scientific research often looks like nothing more than proving the obvious, but such work is essential; nothing should be taken for granted. It was with this thought in mind that two American biologists set out to see whether anteaters really did have sensitive noses.

They used a common technique for testing an animal's senses. The anteater was trained to associate the smell of camphor with food. It learnt that following the smell of camphor it would find food, but if it followed any other smell it would go unrewarded. The anteater was trained by

Silky anteater. In an ant tunnel the long sticky tongue will probe around trapping the insects.

placing it at one end of a T-shaped box, which had camphor in one arm and eucalyptus in the other. The anteater then had to decide which arm to go down: if it followed the camphor it received food. When it had learnt to connect camphor with a reward of food, the smell of camphor in the one arm was gradually diluted with eucalyptus. So now it had to distinguish between eucalyptus and camphor-with-eucalyptus.

The anteater proved to be remarkably good at detecting the smell of camphor when blanketed by eucalyptus. It was not until there was only one part of camphor in 4,000 parts of eucalyptus that the anteater started going down the wrong arm of the box, which showed that it was not able to tell which arm was the right one to get food. Tests were also made with humans in which they were asked to compare mixtures of camphor and eucalyptus. They were unable to detect any smell of camphor when it was in a mixture of one part with 100 parts of eucalyptus.

So the giant anteater has a sense of smell far better developed than ours. An obvious remark perhaps; but it can now be stated without fear of contradiction, and in arithmetical terms, that anteaters' sense of smell is forty times as good as humans'.

class	**Mammalia**
order	**Edentata**
family	**Myrmecophagidae**
genera & species	*Myrmecophaga tridactyla* giant anteater
	Cyclopes didactylus silky anteater
	Tamandua tetradactyla tamandua

Distribution of the anteater family. They are found only in Central and South America, as are the other Edentates, the armadillos and the sloths.

Ant-lion

Ant-lion is the name given to insects of the family Myrmeleontidae, grouped in the order Neuroptera, together with the alderflies (see p 27) and which bear some resemblance to dragonflies, and more particularly to the lacewing flies which they resemble in appearance and habits, in both larval and adult stages. The adults have long thin bodies and two pairs of slender wings of about equal size. Their heads are small with short, thread-like antennae, knobbed at the tips. The largest are little more than 3 in. The name ant-lion is derived from the habits of the larva. This has a short, thick, fleshy body and disproportionately large calliper-like jaws which are armed with strong spines and bristles that help to grasp its prey, mainly ants. These insects, not being found in the British Isles, have no naturally occurring English name, the word ant-lion being a literal translation of the French for them, fourmi-lion. There are several species of ant-lions in the United States, especially in the south and south-west where they have been called doodle bugs for at least a century. The student of etymology may be interested to know that this name was applied independently to the flying bomb in 1944. There are more than 600 species of ant-lion. The typical European species is Myrmeleon formicarius, *the adult of which is about 1 in. long with a wing span of 2 in.*

Habits

Ant-lions are found in woods, forests and plantations wherever there is a sandy soil. The larvae of many species burrow in the sand, the entrance of the burrow being at the bottom of a conical pit, 2 in. deep and 3 in. in diameter at the top, which is also dug by the larva. Groups of these pits can be readily seen in places in southern Europe where the soil is fine and quite dry, and sheltered from the weather, for a shower of rain would destroy the pits and smother the ant-lions. Likely places are the entrances to dry caves, beneath overhanging rocks and trees, below the eaves of houses, and in similar sheltered sites.

The adults are active from June to August, usually at dusk or during the night. Their flight is somewhat feeble and awkward. One reason why this type of insect is named after its larva is because the adults are very inconspicuous even in strong daylight, flying only when the light is failing or has gone, seldom being seen except when attracted to lights.

Pit-trapped victims

Adult ant-lions have been relatively little studied. They are reported to feed on fruit and on small flies, and they may possibly feed on the honey-dew produced by aphids, as do the lacewings. The larva sets and springs one of the most spectacular traps

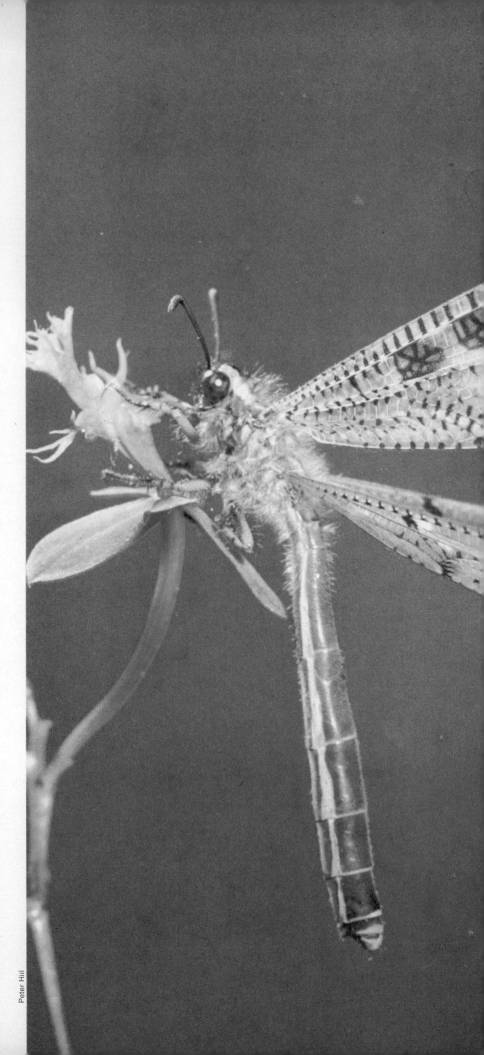

Peter Hill

Ron Taylor

△ *Ant-lion gripping an ant in its vice-like jaws.*
◁ *The delicate beauty of the harmless adult ant-lion is in vivid contrast with its vicious hunting larva.*
▽ *The gigantic calliper-like jaws or mandibles of the ant-lion larva which firmly seize its victim. Together with the secondary jaws or maxillae, two tubes are formed down which flows a paralysing fluid.*

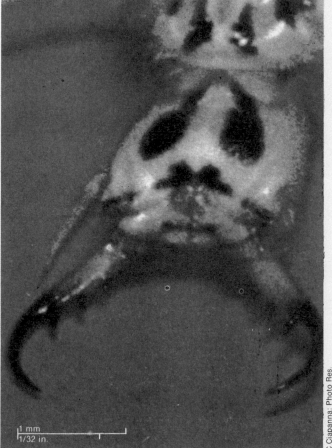

C Ciapanna: Photo Res.

1 mm
1/32 in

1 mm
1/32 in.

in the animal kingdom. Buried at the bottom of its pit, with only camouflaged head and strong jaws exposed, it waits for grains of sand disturbed by a passing ant or spider to fall, and provide a trigger to spring its trap. Immediately sand is scooped on to the head by the jaws and the larvae then jerks its head forwards and upwards, catapulting a stream of sand with great force and accuracy at its intended victim. This barrage, the steep sides of the pit, and the sand being undermined by the ant-lion's digging, together cause the victim to slide down to within reach of the ant-lion's jaws where it is immediately seized.

Sometimes the ant-lion gets only an unsatisfactory grip on its prey. In this event it may toss its victim rapidly against the sides of the pit until it gets a firm hold. It may even temporarily release its victim and again hurl sand at it if it shows signs of escaping. But once firmly held, the prey is drawn partially beneath the sand and then the second function of the calliper-like jaws comes into effect. These jaws are deeply grooved underneath. When the maxillae or secondary mouth parts are pressed against them, together they form two tubes down which a paralysing fluid flows, to be injected into the victim's body. When its struggles have ceased digestive juices are then injected in much the same way. These dissolve the tissues which the ant-lion then sucks up and swallows. Finally, the empty case of the insect's body is tossed up and over the edge of the pit by the ant-lion using the same technique as when catapulting sand grains.

Although the eyes of the larva are well-developed they seem to play no part in detecting the presence of food. If a few grains of sand at the edge of the pit are dislodged so they roll down the side and strike the ant-lion larva in wait at the bottom, it will immediately begin hurling sand upwards. Since it will react in this way when no prey is visible it is a fair assumption that the eyes play little part.

Occasionally ant-lion pits are grouped so close together that there is little chance of the occupants all getting sufficient food. This is offset by the larvae being able to fast without harm for up to 8 months.

Not all species of ant-lion dig pits. Some capture their prey by speed, others do so by stealth or ambush, perhaps lurking beneath stones and rubbish. It is interesting to note that while the highly specialised and somewhat sedentary pit-making species can only walk backwards, the more active species are able to do so in any direction.

Three-year life cycle

After mating, the female ant-lion lays her eggs singly in the sand. These are white and oval, and being sticky on the surface, immediately become encrusted with a layer of sand, which serves as a protective camouflage. Within a day of hatching, the young ant-lion has already dug a pit, of a size proportionate to itself. Thenceforth, the larva goes through three stages known as instars. At the end of each of these, the larva leaves its pit temporarily and hides beneath the sand for about a week to ten days. During this period it casts its old skin, and then digs a new pit and begins to feed

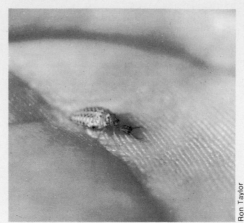

Ant-lion larvae although very vicious are quite small. Here a larva is held in the palm clearly showing its size.

again. Probably the length of time spent as a larva depends to a large extent on the food available. But even with plenty of food it is estimated that the life-cycle from egg to adult takes from 1–3 years, and far longer under unfavourable circumstances. Once fully grown the larva pupates beneath the soil at the bottom of the pit, within a spherical silken cocoon. As in all insects of the order Neuroptera, the silk is produced by the so-called Malpighian tubules, structures named after Malpighi, the 17th-century Italian microscopist who first described them. The silk is given out through the anus. This contrasts with caterpillars of butterflies and moths, for example, whose silk is produced by glands in the head. Almost as soon as the silk makes contact with the air, it hardens and, like the eggs, the cocoon is further protected by sand which sticks to its outer surface, although the innermost layers of silk never become sanded. Only when the cocoon is completed does the ant-lion larva shed its skin for the last time, revealing the cream-coloured pupa. The period of pupation to emergence of the perfect winged insect is usually about a month. Just prior to emergence, the ant-lion pupa cuts a hole in the cocoon with its pupal mandibles, and, using its 'free' pupal legs, crawls part way out of the cocoon before emerging as the perfect insect. At this stage, the pupal skin splits, and the adult works its way to the surface of the soil where it then climbs up a plant or tree from which it can hang while the body hardens and the wings expand and dry.

Built-in trapping technique

Before man settled down to agriculture he lived by hunting and capturing wild animals. No doubt one of the first things he learnt to do was to build a pit in which to trap his quarry. Whether he merely stumbled on the idea or thought it out carefully in the first place is something we shall never know. Whichever way it was, however, he devised various methods of using the pit. He would camouflage it with branches of trees so that the animal passing that way did not suspect a trap. He would plant pointed stakes in the bottom of the pit or lurk nearby ready with a spear to make a kill. These and many variations have been used

for thousands of years and are still in use in various parts of the world even today. All the methods bear some resemblance to the tactics used by the ant-lion. Indeed, some of the things the ant-lion does seem to be an improvement on human techniques and therefore have the appearance of intelligence. We can be fairly sure that man started using pits because his better brain capacity enabled him to see the advantages and also to improve on method. Here is the essential difference between the things that insects do and the things we do. The insect merely follows an inherent behaviour pattern. We would find if we examined the pits and the behaviour of thousands of ant-lions of a given species that each individual trapped its prey in exactly the same way as every other individual of its species. Each ant-lion larva would start with the same method and would continue to use this method throughout its lifetime as a larva, without any improvement on it. Everything it does is therefore inborn or innate.

Nevertheless, those who study insects find themselves being forced to admit that there are times when even insects appear to depart slightly from the inborn pattern of behaviour, to adjust their actions to the varying needs of the moment or to the

Ant-lion trapping pits. Should an ant or spider walk too near this steep-sided pit, it is doomed. The ant-lion disturbs the sand so the victim slides down to be gripped by its waiting jaws.

changing circumstances, in a way which suggests that some sort of thought or some sort of intelligence, no matter how rudimentary, is being brought to bear on it. As a result, scientists now tend to talk about insects having plastic, that is, flexible behaviour. Further examples will be seen in future issues.

class	**Insecta**
order	**Neuroptera**
family	**Myrmeleontidae**
genera	*Myrmeleon, Palpares,* *Hesperoleon, and others*

Aphis

Aphides or 'plant lice' are a group of hemipteran bugs of great economic importance to agriculture as they do considerable harm to crops, both directly, by sucking the cell-sap and indirectly by transmitting certain virus diseases, such as potato leaf-roll and sugar-beet yellows, from one plant to another. There are many species, some 500 in the British Isles alone, but probably the best known are those commonly referred to as greenfly and blackfly by the gardener who finds them, often in depressing numbers, on his roses and broad beans. Aphides have soft, oval bodies, small heads, compound eyes, long 6- or 7-jointed antennae, and a jointed beak or rostrum adapted for piercing plant tissues. Some have transparent wings, the first pair being much the longer. Aphides are usually about 2–3 mm long; rarely more than 5 mm.

N A Callow

A winged black aphid being tended by an ant. Ants will farm large numbers of aphides, tending them carefully and milking them for the honeydew which is secreted by the aphides (approx × 12).

Heavenly pests

Though most familiar as pests of cultivated plants, aphides begin their life on various wild trees and shrubs from which they migrate at intervals to other plants, both wild and in gardens. After mating in late summer or autumn, the black bean aphis *Aphis fabae* for example, lays eggs on the spindle tree or guelder rose. These hatch the following spring as winged females which fly to bean crops where they reproduce by parthenogenesis (that is, without mating). These are called 'stem mothers' as they are the beginning of a new population. Although they may reach the bean plants only singly in many cases, they breed at a tremendous rate forming large colonies, which explains the apparently quite sudden appearance of an infestation where none was visible a day or so previously.

How such a weak, delicate creature as the aphid manages to migrate so successfully from its host plant to another has been investigated thoroughly in recent years. The winged females usually leave the plants where they hatched in two main waves, one in the morning, one in the afternoon. But conditions must be favourable for the movement to take place. It never takes place at night or at temperatures below 17°C/62°F. Once airborne, the aphides are carried up on air currents, often to a great height. After several hours, descending air currents bring the aphides down and they seek out suitable plants. Sample catches taken in nets on balloons at heights up to 2,000 ft show that 30% of clouds of insects floating high up consists of aphides. They may be carried hundreds of miles over land and sea.

In preparing for flight, aphides appear to go through a kind of take-off procedure, which may be repeated several times before actual launching takes place. The centre pair of legs is raised and tucked into the hollow formed by the constriction between thorax and abdomen. Then, balancing on the remaining four legs, the aphid unfolds its wings and takes off. In spite of their apparent fragility, aphides are not easily blown off plants.

The winged females settle on the alternative plants and produce mainly wingless offspring, but some winged individuals are produced at intervals, and these daily leave to seek out other uninfested plants.

Piercing and sucking feeders

As a family, aphides feed on many kinds of plants, but while some species may be catholic in their tastes, others can exist only on one species. The mouth-parts are modified for piercing plant tissues and sucking up the cell-sap, especially from the phloem, the main food stream of the plant. The mandibles and maxillae (mouth-parts) work together as extraordinarily fine needle-like stylets which are thrust deep into the soft parts of the plant. The labium or tongue takes no part in the operation but has a groove in which the stylets are sheathed when not in use. Before feeding actually begins, a salivary secretion is injected into the wound made by the stylets. This prevents the sap coagulating as it flows up the stylets.

While many aphides feed externally on plants, others, far less familiar to us, form 'galls' or enclosed receptacles in which they are able to feed while hidden from the attacks of predators. Examples of aphid gall-makers may be found on trees such as poplars, elms, limes, spruce and cultivated currant bushes. Frequently, the galls form a refuge for passing the winter. In spring and summer a new generation may seek out quite different plants on which to feed without making a gall. In some species, there is simply a migration back and forth from one part of the tree, the leaves and shoots, to the roots. An example is the notorious woolly aphis or American blight of apple trees, which makes a characteristic fluffy 'wool' in which it feeds.

Oddly enough, it is their excretory habit which is undoubtedly the most striking and significant fact about aphides. In feeding, aphides take up large quantities of sap in order to get sufficient protein. The rest, the fluid rich in sugar, is given out through the anus as honeydew, often in great quantities. Being rich in sugars honeydew is much sought after by ants and some other insects.

Young without mating

For most of the year, aphid populations consist only of females which reproduce parthenogenetically at a great rate. Later in the year, winged females fly back to their primary host plants — usually trees — and lay eggs which hatch as males and females. These mate and lay eggs in crevices in the bark, which hatch in the following spring, producing only females — and thus the cycle begins over again.

A single parthenogenetic female may produce as many as 25 daughters in one day, and as these themselves are able to breed in about 8–10 days the numbers of aphides produced by just one female in a season can reach astronomical proportions. It has been estimated that if all the offspring of a single aphid were to survive, and each reproduced and multiplied, there would be in the course of one year sufficient to 'equal the weight of 500,000,000 stout men'. Breeding is slowed down by adverse conditions, especially cold. If aphides are kept warm in a greenhouse, parthenogenetic females are produced continuously without a single male ever seeing the light of day.

Enemies everywhere

Many small insect-eating birds, such as tits and flycatchers, eat aphides. Ladybirds, lacewings, bugs, spiders and hover-fly larvae prey on them. In addition, certain parasitic wasps of the family Braconidae lay their eggs in aphides. The larvae consume the tissues of their hosts and eventually pupate inside the empty husk.

Some aphides have, however, evolved defensive mechanisms to guard against attack from these wasps. The aphides' blood cells secrete a capsule which envelops the parasite larva, arresting its development completely within 24 hours. Others form no capsule but appear to secrete some substance which stops the wasp larva's progress within a short period.

Aphides are also able to deter insect enemies by exuding a kind of wax from a pair of chimney-like stumps, called cornicles, on the rear end. This temporarily paralyses the attacker. Some aphides, too, are apparently so distasteful that a ladybird larva will vomit if it tries to eat one.

Ants, who rear aphides for the sake of their honeydew, also protect their charges from attack by predators. One way they do this is to eat the eggs of potential predators, such as those of ladybirds and hover-flies, which have been deliberately laid near an aphid population.

△ *Greenfly bearing young actually giving birth. The offspring's body is just free of the mother (approx × 20).*

▽ *The young now dangles in mid-air with abdomen, legs and antennae completely free of the mother (approx × 30).*

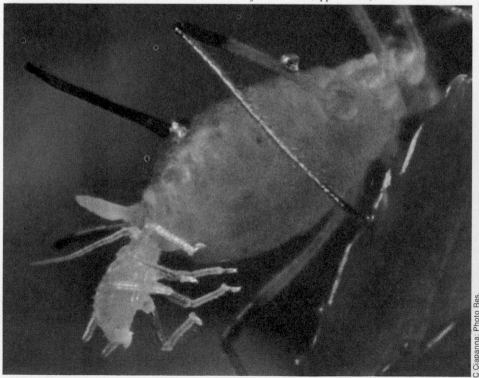

Ants' aphid farm

Long before history, man tamed and domesticated certain animals for his own uses: for pulling loads, for hunting, for companionship, but especially as food. Ants have been doing much the same thing with aphides for infinitely longer. They rear or at least closely associate with them, eating the honeydew and taking it back to the nest for the larva. Just as man is able to stimulate the production of milk in cows and goats, so too can ants encourage production of honeydew in aphides by improving conditions for their existence. This they may do by a variety of means, apart from repelling predators. They may 'herd' their charges, by forcibly confining them to the growing tips of plants which are the most nutritious, thus stimulating growth and breeding and, of course, the emission of honeydew. Where there are no ants present, the honeydew may eventually cover large areas of the plant, causing its death by wilting, by suffocation or by attracting fungi. By removing the aphides' honeydew, the ants ensure their charges' food sources.

Ants also take aphides into their nests, where they may lay eggs, or they may carry the eggs themselves from the plants on which they are laid. After emerging, the young aphides are carefully tended and 'milked' by the ants while they feed on the roots of various plants. Some aphides live only in ants' nests, and never see the light of day. For others, special shelters are built where the aphides can feed, protected from predators. Comparison with the human farmer's cattle-sheds is irresistible.

Presumably, the ants' habit of 'farming' aphides started haphazardly by attacking and killing them for food or simply by licking the drops of fluid which appeared periodically at the insects' vents. Honeydew is not produced continuously and the drop of liquid produced is in normal circumstances discarded by a flick of the aphides' hind leg. Under stimulation from an ant, however, the aphid does not discard the fluid but allows the ant to remove it, and goes on doing so, seeming to enjoy the caressings of the ant's antennae.

Under continued stimulation very large quantities of honeydew may be produced. One large aphid can produce nearly 2 cu mm in an hour, and a colony of the common ant *Lasius fuliginosus* can, it has been estimated, collect about 3−6 lb of honeydew in 100 days.

Control of aphides is something of paramount importance, but always difficult, and it is depressing for the gardener to know that the presence of ants in an aphid colony contributes directly to the increase of the problem. It has been calculated that in accelerating growth and reproduction in aphides and protecting them from predators, ants can indirectly double the loss in the yield of bean plants as compared with when aphides alone are present.

△ *Ants will stimulate aphides to exude honeydew by stroking them with their antennae. One large aphid can produce 2 cu mm/hour.*

▽ *Greenfly on the underside of a sycamore leaf. Trees are often the primary host plants of aphides (approx natural size).*

class	Insecta
order	Hemiptera
sub-order	Homoptera
family	Aphididae

Lacewing hunting aphides

W. Harstrick Photo Res.

1 mm
1/32 in.

The beautiful apollo butterfly, Parnassius phoebus, *resting with wings outstretched.*

Alpine apollo showing its bright spot markings.

Apollo butterfly

One of the family of butterflies known as the swallowtails, not unlike them in shape, but lacking the tail-like appendages on the hind wing which give the family its name. The apollo and its relatives are not brightly coloured, most of them being white, with spots and eye-like markings of black and red. They are nevertheless elegant and beautiful.

Range and habitat

The common apollo is found in mountainous regions of Europe, from Scandinavia to the Alps and Pyrenees, but not in the British Isles. It flies at fairly low altitudes. A related species, the alpine apollo, occurs at higher altitudes. About 30 species of apollo butterflies are known, ranging through Europe and Asia to North America. All are mountain butterflies and some species range up to 20,000 ft in the Himalayas. Owing to their inaccessible habitat some of the Central Asiatic species are extremely rare and highly prized by collectors.

Life history

The caterpillar of the common apollo feeds on orpine, a kind of stonecrop. The caterpillar is black with red spots and, when fully grown, spins a cocoon in which to pupate. Growth is slow and it takes 2 years to complete the life-history. So far as they are known the early stages of all the species are similar, and the larva feed on stonecrops and saxifrages. The habit, very unusual among butterflies, of spinning a cocoon is no doubt correlated with the need for protection from frost at high altitudes.

Only the common apollo habitually flies at low altitudes, and there are indications that some of the bodily structures of apollos as a whole may serve as an alpine kit. The body is covered with hairs, like a fur coat. It is dark in colour, which may help to absorb heat from the sun. The wings, white with black spots, are proportionately larger than in other butterflies, so exposing a greater surface to the sun's rays, and also assisting the butterfly in its unusual soaring habit. Moreover, they are so thinly covered with scales as to be almost translucent, which probably assists the absorption of the sun's heat.

God-like butterflies

Apollo butterflies have been seen in the Alps soaring above hillsides on uprising wind currents with wings outstretched and motionless. Soaring flight, common in birds, is rare among insects. Apollo was a Greek god of the mountains and the vegetation and later the sun god. All this makes the choice of name for these butterflies singularly apt. The god-like character is, however, marred by a North American species, *Parnassius autocrator*. The caterpillar, brilliant orange in colour, gives off a most unpleasant odour from just behind its head whenever danger threatens. All apollo larvae (and swallowtail too) have an organ (the osmaterium) behind the head that gives off an odour, but this is usually faint and at any rate not unpleasant to the human nose.

class	**Insecta**
order	**Lepidoptera**
family	**Papilionidae**
genus	***Parnassius***

Pyrenees mountains where the alpine apollo can be found at high altitudes. The common apollo lives at much lower altitudes in mountainous regions from Scandinavia to the Alps and Pyrenees.

Caterpillar of European apollo Parnassius apollo, *which takes nearly 2 years to grow.*

Apus ventral view showing its many limbs.

John Clegg

Apus

A small, primitive, freshwater crustacean, apus is distantly related to the more familiar crabs, lobsters, shrimps and crayfish. Originally its scientific name was Apus cancriformis, *but it is now called* Triops cancriformis, *and apus has been adopted as its common name. Although apus is quite common in several parts of the world, notably in southern Europe, it is extremely rare and of uncertain appearance in Britain. Coloured brownish or olive-green, it is usually about 1 in. in body length, although specimens up to 2 in. have been recorded. It has many pairs of limbs when fully grown, each ending in several filaments, and at its rear is a pair of long-whip-like appendages or furcae. The head and thorax are covered by a large carapace which gives apus a superficial resemblance to the horseshoe crab.*

Habits and habitat
Apus generally lives in temporary pools where there are no fish or other predators. It can only live and breed satisfactorily in warm conditions, and this partly accounts for its extreme rarity in Britain where temporary pools are more likely to occur during the colder months of autumn and winter. Apus swims on its back, by means of the almost non-stop wavelike motion of its many trunk limbs and their filaments. This action probably also helps in respiration, by creating currents that wash over the gills, so increasing the amount of oxygen taken in. In polluted ponds, or in those otherwise deficient in oxygen, some apus develop the oxygen carrying chemical, haemoglobin, in the blood which further increases their ability to take up dissolved oxygen from the water; such individuals are usually coloured bright red. The tail filaments, or furcae, besides acting as rudders, probably function as posterior antennae, giving warning of any attack from the rear. Apus has two compound eyes set close together near the leading edge of the carapace and another single eye is on the underside.

Apus has been known to science for less than 250 years, the first published record of its existence being in 1732. It was first recorded from Britain, at Bexley, in 1738, and then only twice more until 1907 when it turned up in Kirkcudbrightshire, Scotland. Although none was found when the same Scottish ponds were searched the following year, apus was again discovered in Kirkcudbrightshire, in ponds near the original ones, in 1948. Now it seems lost again as a result of coastal erosion. Hampshire can, so far, boast the best tally of apus in Britain, the crustacean having been discovered there in 1816, 1934, 1947, 1948 and 1949.

Filter feeder
Apus feeds on algae and other small organisms such as insect larvae which it may find by grubbing in the mud at the bottom of the pond or pool in which it lives. Some food is got from the water itself, the rapidly pulsating limbs helping to collect and transfer minute food particles to the animal's mouth. Apus will also eat larger animals and even dead or dying of its own kind. Such food is mostly shredded by the tough chitinous teeth, present at the bases of the trunk limbs, or by the mandibles.

Reproduction by self-fertilization
Male apus are rarely found in Britain, or in northern Europe, and it was once thought that the females reproduced by parthenogenesis (that is, development of unfertilised eggs). More recent research, however, has indicated that the supposed females are more likely to be self-fertile hermaphrodites. Males and females do occur in warmer climates (for example, in North Africa) and then sexual reproduction does take place.

There is in the main a very rapid development to maturity, the period from hatching to adulthood being often as little as a fortnight. In this way, reproduction can be effected before the pond or pool dries up again. Although the adults die when the water has evaporated, the eggs can survive long periods of drought, and may in fact remain dormant for several years. They have a hard outer casing which prevents them from drying up. If, however, an egg is immersed in sunlit water at a suitable temperature ($30°-35°C/85°-95°F$) the shell soon breaks open and a young apus emerges, still enclosed in a transparent bag-like mem-

Natural History Museum

△ *Cambrian Trilobite. Apus may have evolved from an early form of trilobite over 500 million years ago, during the Cambrian period. It has hardly changed for 180 million years.*

▷ *Living fossil. Apus as well as resembling the trilobites looks very similar to the horseshoe crab, because of the large carapace which covers the head and thorax (×10).*

brane. Following a short resting period, the envelope is broken and the tiny apus, which is only about $\frac{1}{2}$ mm long at birth, swims away. Thenceforth, it passes through a number of different stages quite unlike the adult in form. At each stage, a new body segment appears, the limbs become more numerous, and the forked tail filaments increase in length. When adult, the trunk consists of 33 segments, each of them, except the last five, bearing up to five pairs of limbs. Apus is thus unique among living crustaceans in having many more pairs of limbs than it has body segments: some authorities mention as many as 71 pairs.

One of the most remarkable features of the life-history of this quite extraordinary

John Clegg

crustacean is the way the size and form of the limbs change, as well as the use to which they are put, as the animal grows up. To start with it has only three pairs of limbs, one of which forms the antennae; the second pair, antennules (secondary antennae) and the third pair, jaws. Soon the antennules and the jaws become relatively smaller and the young apus propels itself with its long antennae. Then the true limbs begin to appear, increase in number with each moult, and take over the function of propulsion. The antennae now become shorter with each moult, and finally are so small they are difficult to see. The antennules diminish too, almost to vanishing point, while the jaws not only change in shape but also grow much stronger. The antennae carry the sense organs, but as they become smaller their sensory functions are taken over by the true limbs (usually spoken of as the trunk limbs).

Living fossil

Apus and the horseshoe crab, although superficially alike, are not very closely related, but they may well have had a common ancestry. The earliest known ancestors of horseshoe crabs were the fossil Trilobites and it is likely that an early form of Trilobite may also have been the ancestor of apus. The various stages through which apus passes before reaching maturity look very like the larval horseshoe crabs, which in turn resemble Trilobites. One of the most interesting things about apus is that it has survived virtually unchanged since the Triassic period about 180,000,000 years ago. Indeed some scientists consider that the species we know today is actually the very same species that was living all that time ago. This is a very long time for an actual species to survive unchanged. Usually when we speak of a living fossil we mean an animal, or a plant, that is very like those that died out a long time ago. One reason why apus has managed to survive such an unimaginable length of time may lie in its ability to produce vast numbers of eggs (frequently without the necessity of a male) which can remain dormant, resisting heat and cold alike, perhaps for many years. That is why it is apt to pop up like a jack-in-a-box, in places where it was previously unknown.

We do not know as yet how the eggs of apus are spread. They are probably picked up on birds' feet in mud which later falls off as it dries. By sheer chance these may lie where a temporary pool is formed during a warm, wet spell. Theoretically, therefore, apus can turn up almost anywhere within its geographical range, even in a temporary pool in your back yard! Perhaps if people looked for it more often we might have more records of its distribution.

class	**Crustacea**
sub-class	**Branchiopoda**
order	**Notostraca**
genus & species	***Triops (Apus) cancriformis***

75

Arapaima

The arapaima, said to be one of the largest freshwater fishes, is rather like a pike. It has a long cylindrical body, with the unpaired fins set well back towards the tail, a small flattened head, and a jutting lower jaw. The fish is coloured green in front but the rear half of the body becomes increasingly reddish, the tail being crimson. In Brazil it is known as the pirarucu, pirá meaning fish and urucú being the name of a bush in Brazil bearing flaming red seeds from which is made the annato dye, used for colouring cheese and butter. In Peru it is known as paiche. It probably also occurs in Venezuela, Colombia, and Guyana.

Freshwater fishes are generally smaller than marine fishes, and only a few of them attain giant size. The arapaima is one of the larger ones and is said to reach nearly 15 ft in length and 440 lb in weight, but usually it is 7—8 ft long. The family to which it belongs is characterised by stout, bony scales each containing canals that form a mosaic-like pattern. Rings on the scales indicate age. The arapaima matures at 4 to 5 years and can live 18 years or more.

The arapaima is placed in the family Osteoglossidae or bony tongues, fishes with a lineage that can be traced back over 100 million years. So the arapaima is a living fossil, and some of its more primitive features are the bony head, peculiar shape of the fins, lobe-like tail and the lung-like air-bladder.

△ A gigantic arapaima about to grab a tasty fish. The operculum which covers the gills has been raised so the gill arches are visible. The rings on the large scales indicate the fish's age. A lifespan of over 18 years is not unknown.

▷ The arapaima can grow to over 5 ft in length in 5 years from birth. Certain features, such as the head, the shape of the fins, the lobe-like tail and the lung-like swimbladder, indicate its primitiveness. Its family can be traced back over 100 million years.

WT Davidson

Klaus Paysan

Air breathing habit

The arapaima keeps to shallow water where it moves about lethargically, periodically rising to the surface to gulp air into the swim-bladder, which opens by a duct into the back of the throat, functioning as a lung. The swim-bladder is large and occupies the whole area above the gut. It is made of cellular, lung-like tissue, and it opens direct into the gullet. This system is probably aided by the arapaima's large human-like red blood corpuscles. (The blood also clots on exposure to air—another development in the direction of land-living.) This development of air breathing apparatus recalls that of lungfishes, and it is of interest that the Osteoglossidae have nearly the same distribution as the lung-fishes (see map), and both provide evidence suggesting that all continents were once joined and have drifted apart (see amphisbaena for similar evidence for the theory of continental drift).

Omnivorous feeder

Though essentially a fish eater, the arapaima seems ready to eat anything. The fish it preys upon include the hassar, lukamani, and baira, but examination of 5,000 stomachs revealed the remains of many other items, including water snails, freshwater shrimps, worms, vegetable matter, freshwater turtles, snakes, frogs, crabs, grasshoppers, pebbles, sand, mud, and even coal. The young fry feed on microplankton, later take general plankton, and as they increase in size they take plankton and small fishes. When the young have reached this last stage they stand a risk of being eaten by their parents. There is an interesting adaptation of the fourth gill-arch, which was once thought to help in breathing. In one of the five species in the family this has now been shown to be a filter, which strains small particles from the water passing across the gills. These are trapped in mucus which is then carried to the gullet and stomach. When the water-level is low, in the dry season, this food is important.

Parental care

The breeding season lasts from December to May. Spawning takes place in shallow water, at depths of 2½–5 ft. During April and May, when the rivers overflow and flood the low-lying land, the arapaima move into this shallow water, select sandy areas clear of vegetation and hollow out nests, digging with mouth, chin, and fins. These saucer-like nests are 20 in. across and up to 8 in. deep.

Normally there is little difference between male and female, but at the breeding season the female goes a chestnut shade, the male develops a black head and his tail turns a bright vermilion. Each female lays up to 180,000 eggs in several batches, each in its separate nest. The eggs, ⅛–¼ in. in diameter, hatch in 5 days. The larvae, ½ in. long and black, swarm in a group over the male's head near the surface. So as he rises to gulp air the larvae swarming round his black head are made invisible. They also swarm round his head when disturbed, protected no doubt by this camouflage. The female, meanwhile, swims around father and offspring, ready to drive off intruders.

Enemies

It is caught and eaten in large numbers, its flesh being salted or dried. The aboriginal American Indians kill it with bow and arrow or trap it in the shallows. Jaguars also are said to catch arapaima.

Not so big

While its lineage and anatomy are in little doubt, the arapaima's size has been the subject of much speculation. Nearly every book on fishes, every dictionary and encyclopedia, tells us that the arapaima reaches 15 ft in length and a weight of 400 or even 600 lb. This, it seems, is a myth. The fish is extensively eaten and therefore must be very well known. The numbers caught annually are high, as indicated by the investigator who, wishing to catalogue the things the arapaima eats, examined 5,000 stomachs in a short while. Yet nobody has so far recorded, from actual measurements, one longer than 7 ft or a greater weight than 246 lb.

When we look into this we find that the naturalist Schomburgk, writing in 1836 about his visit to Guiana, stated that 'the natives' told him 'the fish reached 15 ft long and 400 lb weight'. Every writer since has repeated these figures, most of them being unaware that the evidence was hearsay. Other writers have aided and abetted by using such phrases as 'too long and wide to fit into a 15-ft canoe' or 'I estimate 300 to 400 lb because one fish filled up to busting point 181 Indians. . . .'

Since Schomburgk's day hundreds of thousands of arapaima have been caught and eaten, many thousands have been examined by scientists. Yet the largest recorded is still only 7 ft.

class	**Pisces**
order	**Osteoglossiformes**
family	**Osteoglossidae**
genus & species	***Arapaima gigas***

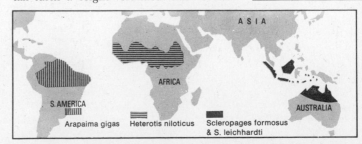

Distribution of the Osteoglossidae. Note the discontinuous distribution through South America, Africa, the Malay Archipelago and Australia.

ASIA

AFRICA

S. AMERICA

AUSTRALIA

Arapaima gigas   Heterotis niloticus   Scleropages formosus & S. leichhardti

Archerfish

Any of five species of fishes, which reach up to 1 ft in length, noted for obtaining insects by shooting them down with a stream of water drops. The first accurate account of this was written in 1765 by the Dutch governor of a hospital in Batavia (now Jakarta) the capital of Java. The governor decided to send a specimen to Europe, with his description, but by a mistake he sent a long-nosed butterfly fish. Scientists studied the report and also the specimen and not surprisingly they could not see how this fish could spit water several feet. In any event, the butterfly fish lives in the sea, on coral reefs, where insects do not normally fly. Consequently, the story of the archerfish was disbelieved until 1902, when a Russian scientist obtained some specimens, kept them in an aquarium and verified their shooting abilities.

Distribution and habitat
Archerfishes extend from India through south-east Asia, the Malay Archipelago, and parts of Australia to the Philippines. Their habitat is mainly the brackish waters of mangrove belts, but they may also live in the sea, or go up streams into fresh water.

Hamburgers for dinner
Their main food consists of small water animals swimming or floating near the surface, but when hungry, archerfishes shoot down insects crawling on leaves and stems of overhanging vegetation. A fully-grown adult is able to hit insects 6 ft above the surface of the water. Indeed, one fish has been seen to miss its target and the jet of water travel a measured 15 ft. If it misses with the first jet it will follow with several more in rapid succession. At the moment of shooting, the tip of the snout is just breaking water, the eyes being submerged. Water in the gill-chambers is driven into the mouth by a sudden powerful compression of the gill-covers. At the same time the tongue is pressed upwards, converting a groove in the roof of the mouth into a tube, which increases the speed of the outgoing stream.

Archerfishes begin to 'spit' when very young and only a few centimetres long, but the jets of water they produce do not travel much over 4 in. As they grow so their marksmanship improves and the length to which they spit increases.

Earl S Herald has described how, at Steinhart Aquarium, in the United States, one of the most popular exhibits was 150 archerfishes in a tank which were fed daily. The level of water in the tank was lowered and finely ground hamburger thrown against the exposed glass walls of the tank. The fishes would reconnoitre, then one bolder than the rest would leap out of the water to the distance of 1 ft in an endeavour to knock the food down. Eventually all the fishes would bombard it with drops of water and in 15 minutes about ⅓ lb of ground hamburger would be washed down from the glass.

Michael Tweedie has recalled visiting the Aquarium at Batavia in 1934 and leaning over the tank to watch the archerfishes. He received drops of water on the cheek, which stung sharply. Other observers have noted that the normal blinking of their eyelids stimulates an archerfish to shoot at them.

Breeding
The adults apparently spawn far from land, in the regions of coral rock or coral reef. The young return to the brackish water or even beyond, into the fresh water. They have the dark bars on the back, as in adults, and they also have 'light-flecks', yellow iridescent flecks on the back between the dark bars. At times the flecks shine so brightly they appear like tiny greenish fluorescent lights. It is suggested they may act as recognition marks between members of the species, helping them keep together in the muddy water.

Sharpshooter
For 137 years disbelief and an air of mystery surrounded the activities of archerfishes. For a further 59 years there was a second mystery within the first: how does the archerfish with its eyes below water judge distance and take aim at targets in the air above? If a stick is dipped at an angle into water, it appears bent due to the bending of light rays as they pass from air into water. This is known as refraction. The archerfish will therefore see its food in a different position from the true one and yet it still manages to carry out very good sharpshooting. It was assumed that the archerfish in some way allowed for refraction. In 1961, however, the truth was realised, just by more careful observation of an archerfish feeding on insects. It swims forward until it is almost under its target, appears to take aim, then as it ejects the water jet, it jerks its body nearly to the vertical. In this position, just as a stick dipped straight into the water does not look bent, because refraction is reduced to a minimum, so the archerfish, looking straight up out of the water, sees the exact position of its insect target.

It has been noted that archerfishes sometimes miss their target. This is probably when, over-eager to take aim, they shoot their water drops before they have positioned themselves as nearly vertical as possible.

All the same, it is the general opinion that archerfishes are relatively intelligent. That their marksmanship improves with practice indicates learning ability.

Curiouser and curiouser
The idea that archerfishes are unusually intelligent seems to be based largely on the kind of eyes they possess. These are large and more highly organized than in most fish, and give binocular vision, that is, they are forward facing, with a large overlap of vision, thus enabling the fish to focus well and judge distances accurately. This is only one of the specializations. Others are the shape of the mouth and tongue and the mechanism for producing a jet of water, as well as the behavioural adaptations

associated with them. When an animal has many adaptations to one end we assume these have been brought about by pressure of natural selection and are therefore necessary for its survival. The strange thing is that in spite of its elaborate equipment for shooting down insects, an archerfish does not use this as the main way of obtaining food. Indeed, it can get along quite well without using it. Archerfishes that live in the sea, for example, apparently never shoot insects down.

Perhaps even more odd is the way the fish will use its jet when quite unnecessary, and this seems to contradict the idea of unusual intelligence. Archerfishes will catch insects flying low over the water by leaping up and seizing them with the mouth. They have also been seen to aim their jet of water at insects already fallen on the surface, which they could easily have snapped up directly. They have been seen, in addition, to direct a jet as a small object, edible or inedible, lying on the bottom. The jet is not then visible but its trajectory can be appreciated by the sudden compression of the fish's gill-covers and the puff of sand or mud raised at the point of impact. Perhaps the archerfish instinctively 'shoots' at any interesting target and its intelligence is limited to improving its accuracy.

class	**Pisces**
order	**Perciformes**
family	**Toxotidae**
genus & species	***Toxotes jaculatrix***

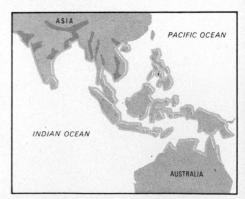

The tropical distribution of the archerfish. They prefer the brackish waters of the mangrove belts, but will live in the sea as well as entering the fresh water streams on the coast.

Archerfish shooting accurately aimed drops of water at a ladybird target. Water in the gill-chambers is ejected via a groove in the roof of the mouth by sudden compression of the gill-covers. Archerfish have been known to hit insects at a distance of 6 ft.▷

Arctic fox

The Arctic fox is very similar in appearance to the common red fox except that it is a little smaller. In winter its coat becomes very long, making it look bulky, and its ears and muzzle are short so that it looks almost cat-like. Both long coat and short ears are adaptations to living in the far north. The small surface area of the ears prevents excessive loss of body-heat, while the thick coat acts as an excellent insulation, keeping heat in.

In summer the coat is greyish-yellow, with white on the underparts, the whole turning white or cream in winter. The 'blue' fox is a variety of Arctic fox that has a bluish-grey coat throughout the year. The proportion of 'blue' foxes varies in different regions. They are common around coasts and on islands, where there is less snow in the winter. In western Greenland as many as half the total number of foxes may be 'blue'. On the Canadian mainland, this number drops to 1% of the total.

A further adaptation to life in polar regions is the growth of long hairs on the soles of the feet, just as on the soles of the polar bear. The hairs probably help the foxes to keep their footing on ice, as well as providing insulation.

From Arctic Circle to the Pole

The range of the Arctic fox covers the treeless tundra that extends round the Arctic regions of Europe, Asia and North America, and includes Greenland, Iceland, Spitsbergen, and Scandinavia, where foxes are found in the mountains around the northern coasts of Finland and Norway. In winter they move farther south, reaching the province of Quebec, in Canada, and southern Norway and Sweden, in Europe. Arctic foxes are to be found on the smallest and most remote islands north of Canada and Greenland, where there are no other land mammals, except polar bears. The foxes reach these almost inaccessible places by travelling across the pack ice, swimming between the ice floes when necessary. They have been found on pack ice within 300 miles of the North Pole, where they apparently feed on the remains of seals killed by polar bears and on fish.

Arctic foxes live a more communal and nomadic life than the red fox, often forming small bands ranging the countryside for food. They are also less wary, and in remote areas show no fear of humans, often coming into camps to pilfer food, or out of sheer curiosity. They do not hibernate and, experimentally, have withstood temperatures of $-73°C/-100°F$.

Opportunist feeder

Arctic foxes eat a wide variety of food, depending on where they live. Towards the southern end of the range food is plentiful, at least in summer when there will be large numbers of birds, lemmings, voles and hares, but the winter of an Arctic island is a lean season and the foxes must take advantage of any source of food.

In the European sector the main food of Arctic foxes is the lemming, so much so that the numbers of foxes increase and decrease with the explosive rises and fall of the lemming populations. Where lemmings and voles, another major item of food, are scarce (or absent as in Iceland) the Arctic foxes search for other food. They will take hares, fish, reindeer calves and berries, or roam the seashores, feeding on shellfish and carrion.

Arctic foxes are the main predator of many birds, especially ground nesting species such as ducks, gulls, and shore birds, taking eggs, young, and, if possible, adults. Many of these, however, have their own tricks to avoid being caught and fox predation is mainly on the weak or unwary.

Nesting on cliffs is a very successful way of avoiding foxes and many sea-birds such as kittiwakes and auks are free from danger. Other birds may be safe on small islands but if the foxes manage to get across to them whole colonies may be wiped out. Arctic jaegers, terns, divers and pink-footed geese defend their nests with force while others such as the eider duck rely on camouflage, sitting motionless on the nest with a good chance of not being noticed.

During the summer, when food is abundant, the Arctic foxes kill more than they immediately need. The surplus is carried back to their dens where it is stored under stones and in crannies for use during the lean times of winter. These caches may contain considerable stores of food. One has been described as holding some 50 lemmings and 30 or 40 little auks, neatly arranged with heads bitten off and tails pointing in the same direction.

In the pack ice of the far north the Arctic fox follows the polar bear in the same way as jackals have been said to follow lions and other carnivores in the tropics to feed on the leftovers from their kills. During the Arctic winter every polar bear is said to be followed by two or three foxes, patiently waiting for the bear to find and kill a seal. In the spring the polar bears' seal hunting is thought essential to the survival of the foxes as there is no other food for them. If they can find a bear to follow, the foxes are pretty well assured of a reasonable supply of food, for, unless it is very hungry, the bear eats only the blubber, and the foxes are left with the meat and entrails.

The polar bear's method of catching a

◁ *Arctic fox searching for food. A hunting polar bear is often followed for food. The foxes wait until the bear has finished with its kill, then eat the leftovers of meat and entrails.*

▷ *Arctic fox,* Alopex lagopus, *crouching in snow. The thick coat is an excellent insulation; the ears are small to reduce excessive body-heat loss.*

▽ *The Arctic fox, covering a large Arctic area, is found within 300 miles of the Pole.*

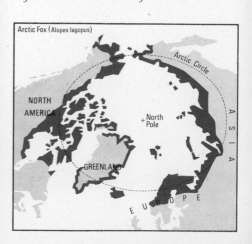

Arctic Fox (Alopex lagopus)

Arctic Circle

NORTH AMERICA

ASIA

North Pole

GREENLAND

EUROPE

seal is to rip open the dome of snow over the breathing hole in the ice and pull the seal out with its paw. It is under this dome that the seal bears her pup and nurses it. Although it may be covered by several feet of snow, bears can scent it, as can the foxes who will dig down to the nursery to take the pup before its mother can rescue it.

Adjustable reproduction
The breeding season begins in April and the cubs are born in May or June after a gestation of 6 weeks. The usual litter is 5–8, but when lemmings are at their peak of abundance, litters of 20 cubs have been known. The male parent stays with the family, helping to feed the cubs and mating with the female again a few weeks after the first litter is born. The second litter is born in July or August and the family splits up in the autumn.

Friend into enemy
Polar bears sometimes attack Arctic foxes, especially if they are very hungry, and they

may well lash out with a paw if the foxes come too close while they are feeding. The foxes may also attack and kill one of their own number, under the same circumstances, or if one is injured.

Carnivore's tidy mind
It has been claimed that a weasel was once seen to kill a number of mice and lay them neatly in a row, cover them with earth and leaves, then kill more mice and lay these in a row on top of the first. Naturalists tend to be sceptical of this, and in natural history, as in any other field of argument, to test an observation that seems to strain credulity one looks for comparable examples.

There is the case of a domestic cat which was fully authenticated. The cat found a nest of the common rat, killed each of the babies in turn and carried it down a garden path for a distance of 20 ft, turned left along another path and there laid each dead baby rat side-by-side to a total of nine, in as neat a row as anyone could devise.

Returning to the story of the weasel we have only to imagine the weasel scraping earth and leaves over the first row before continuing the second lot of killing to see how the episode of the domestic cat lends credence to what otherwise appears a tall story. Now we have the Arctic fox which habitually does something very like the weasel is supposed to have done and the domestic cat is known to have done. All three are carnivores; and if one species of animal does something either habitually or frequently we can reasonably expect this same sort of behaviour to crop up, if only occasionally, in other animals of the same type. The survival value of such behaviour is obvious in a snow-dwelling animal.

class	**Mammalia**
order	**Carnivora**
family	**Canidae**
genus & species	***Alopex lagopus***

Argonaut

In Greek mythology the argonauts were a company of 50 heroes who sailed with Jason when he went in search of the golden fleece. The Greeks also knew about the marine animal we know as the argonaut, or paper nautilus, a sort of cuttlefish which lays its eggs in a white paper-thin shell, the female brooding them. There arose from this a second myth, which persisted until relatively recent times, based on the shape of two of the female's arms, sometimes called tentacles. The argonaut is only distantly related to the cuttlefish, one difference between them being that a cuttlefish has ten arms whereas the argonaut has eight. In the female argonaut two of these are racquet-shaped, and it used to be believed that she sat in her shell, as in a boat, and held these flattened tentacles aloft to act as sails. This was what Aristotle, the Greek zoologist, thought. Moreover, he declared that the remaining arms were used as oars. So for 2,000 years the argonaut was famed as a graceful little navigator that sailed the seas in a shell-boat.

Habits and habitat

The six species of argonaut, all alike except to the specialist, inhabit the warm seas, usually swimming near the surface but capable of going deeper. At times they appear in large numbers in an area where normally they are found only occasionally. In 1936, for example, there was a plague of argonauts and octopuses in the Adriatic.

Normal colouring is in shades of reddish-brown, green, blue and violet, the last two colours being characteristic of the normal arms. The web of the racquet-shaped arms is silvery, and all colours tend to be iridescent. For respiration water is drawn in through a valve behind each eye, passed through the mantle cavity in which the gills lie, and is ejected through the siphon (funnel). The breathing rate, as indicated by pulsations of the whole body, is about 46 beats a minute.

Jet propelled movement

Far from using its arms for sailing and rowing, the six normal arms are tucked into the shell and the argonaut progresses like any octopus, squid or cuttlefish, using jets of water ejected through its siphon to drive itself backwards through the water, and also to steer itself. Sometimes argonauts have been seen taking a ride on jellyfishes, but this is rare and nothing is known of its significance. Only rarely does the animal leave its shell and then only temporarily. If permanently deprived of it the argonaut cannot survive, although apparently it can repair a broken shell.

The shell acts as a hydrostatic organ, giving buoyancy by means of air trapped in its apex. How the air is lost or replaced, to enable the animal to sink or rise, is unknown.

Feeding by touch?

Our knowledge is limited to observations of

Female argonaut swims backwards by ejecting water via her siphon. The male is 1/20 her length.

Peter David

argonauts kept in aquaria. The eye shows no signs of focussing ability or variation in pupil-size, suggesting the animal does not actively pursue prey. Also, when a fish touches the surface of one of the racquet-shaped arms one of the other arms is swept across, as if the argonaut were trying by touch to locate and catch the animal responsible. Presumably its prey is fish, but the only evidence we have is from captive animals that have accepted small fishes.

Sperm in a broken arm

The female, up to 1 ft, including the arms, is 20 times the length of the male, which rarely exceeds $\frac{1}{2}$ in. long. The first arm on each side, in the female, is expanded into an oval membrane, rich in glands which secrete calcium carbonate to form the fluted shell, sculptured with parallel ridges. Each flattened arm secretes half the shell and where the two halves join, a keel is formed, decorated with two rows of brown knobs, corresponding to the suckers on the arms. Her eggs, each $\frac{3}{4}$ mm in diameter, stalked and massed in clumps of 500–600, are attached to the prow of the

The male fertilises the female without meeting.

Popperfoto

2 mm
1/10 in.

shell. The male apparently lives free in the plankton, but has occasionally been found riding in the female's shell. There is no need, however, for male and female to meet even for breeding. Fertilisation is effected by one of the male's arms, loaded with sperm, finding its way to the female. This arm, known as the hectocotylus, is quite extraordinary. It is enclosed in a sac. Sperm pass into a reservoir at the base of the hectocotylus. When this has received its quota of sperms the hectocotylus unwinds, bursts through the thin wall of the enclosing envelope and is ready to break away from the base of the arm, to swim or crawl independently through the water to the female. The middle part of the hectocotylus has up to 50 pairs of suckers and its outer third is long and filamentous; both suckers and the whip-like filament help the hectocotylus to cling to the female's arms until the sperms have fertilised her.

The offspring's development is unknown.

Eaten by fish and dolphins

Quantities of argonaut beaks have been found in the stomachs of sailfish, dolphins and certain large swordfish.

Confusion confounded

On every hand we find huge gaps in our knowledge of the argonaut, and much of what we do possess is not of recent date. In 1827 Delle Chiaje, an Italian scientist, captured an argonaut and found on it what he described as a parasitic worm. Delle Chiaje watched the worm swim and crawl in water for hours on end. Two years later, Baron Cuvier, the French scientist, was sent five of these worm-like organisms beset with nearly a hundred suckers. He agreed they were parasitic worms and gave the supposed species the name *Hectocotylus* (roughly translatable as hollow worm bearing a hundred suckers).

In 1845, Albert Kolliker, Swiss scientist, examined the *Hectocotylus* and came to the conclusion it was the male argonaut which had joined the female in her shell to mate with her. Kolliker was so convinced of this that in 1849 he published a detailed description of the blood-vessels, breathing apparatus and digestive organs of this supposed male argonaut. Four years later, Heinrich Müller found in the straits of Messina several tiny 'octopuses' each with seven arms and an oval sac, and within the sac the long arm with its hundred suckers and sperm reservoir. These were the male argonaut.

The female argonaut has long been famous while the male enjoyed obscurity and anonymity. What little limelight has latterly been turned on him has been directed at the hectocotylus which acts as a reproductive organ and is, in fact, only one part of him, his eighth arm.

phylum	**Mollusca**
class	**Cephalopoda**
order	**Dibranchia**
genus & species	***Argonauta argo***

Nine-banded armadillo, Dasypus novemcinctus, *is the most widely spread of the armadillos.*

Armadillo

There are 20 species of armadillo, grouped in nine genera and distributed through America from Argentina to the south-eastern corner of the United States.

The best-known is the nine-banded armadillo that ranges northwards from South America into Kansas and Missouri in the United States. It has been studied in detail because it is of economic importance, eating eggs, undermining buildings and starting erosion on the one hand, but on the other it kills undesirable insects and snakes.

The largest is the giant armadillo of the forests of eastern South America which has a 3ft body and can weigh as much as 130 lb. It is unusual in having up to a hundred small teeth, more than twice the normal complement for a mammal. The naked-tailed armadillos of central and southern America have five large claws on the front feet. The middle claw is especially large and sickle-shaped. The three-banded armadillo, or apara, of Bolivia, Matto Grosso, Argentina and Brazil is the only armadillo to have a carapace separated from the skin around the sides of the body. It is the only one able to roll up, and the separation of the carapace from the skin means there is room for the head, legs and tail when it does so.

The fairy armadillo of the plains of western Argentina is a strange creature. It has less armour than the other species. The carapace is made up of bands hinged together and covering the back only. Attachment to the body is limited to a narrow ridge of flesh running down the spine. There is another flat shield consisting of a single plate covering the rump; the

armoured tail sticks through this. The rest of the body is covered with a fine, soft, white fur. The fairy armadillo is mole-like, having powerful front legs, and small eyes. It spends more time underground than other armadillos.

The pygmy armadillo, pichi, or pichiciego, that lives in Patagonia and the Argentine pampas, is said to hibernate, but there has been no confirmation of an early report on this habit.

Home and habits

Many armadillos are nocturnal. They live in burrows when not active, sometimes solitarily and sometimes in groups. The nine-banded armadillos will share burrows, only one sex being found in any one burrow. The burrows are 2–3 ft beneath the surface and are not branched.

Rivers are no obstacles to armadillos, for although they are proportionately heavy with their coats of armour, they gain added buoyancy by swallowing air to blow up the intestine. The nine-banded armadillo is said to be able to submerge for 6 minutes.

Some armadillos have an unusual gait. The soles of the hind feet are pressed against the ground but the fore feet are raised up on the strong pointed claws.

Omnivorous feeders

Armadillos live on a variety of food: insects and other invertebrates, plants, carrion and small vertebrates such as snakes and lizards. Giant armadillos have been reported to have dug into new graves to eat the corpses. Naked-tailed armadillos feed mainly on ants and termites, cutting open their runs with their sickle-like claws and extracting the insects with their long, extensible tongues.

Hairy armadillos burrow under, and sometimes into, carcasses to get at maggots and will also dig into soft soil for grubs and insects in a most unusual manner. They force their head into the ground, then twist the body round to make a conical hole.

These armadillos have been seen killing snakes by cutting them with the hard edges of the carapaces.

Armadillo quads

Except for the nine-banded armadillos, breeding habits are not well known. Male armadillos mark their home range with urine, in much the same way as a domestic dog or cat. This habit was responsible for the deaths of several armadillos in early zoo collections. Whenever the cage was cleaned a male armadillo would re-mark his territory, carrying it out with such thoroughness that he would die of dehydration.

The nine-banded armadillo mates in July and August, the female lying on her back during courtship. A single egg is fertilised and then lies free in the uterus for a period of time before becoming embedded in the uterine wall when development can continue. This process, in which development of the embryo does not take place immediately, is called delayed implantation. Gestation takes 120 days.

One to four young are born each year, depending on the species. In the nine-banded armadillos there are four in a litter and they are always identical, in sex as well as other characters. These are identical quads, all of them springing from a single egg and all attached by umbilical cords to a single placenta. This is the area of the uterine wall specialised for transferring food, etc, between the blood of the mother and that of the embryos. In other mammals such multiple births are accidental, and rare, but it is the rule in this armadillo.

The young are born with a soft leathery skin which hardens after a few days.

Protective armour

The name armadillo is derived from the diminutive of the Spanish word 'armado', one that is armed. Body armour in mammals is generally made of compressed hair, as in the plates of pangolins and the horns of rhinoceros, but the armour of armadillos is

Hairy armadillo. The large curved claws are used to dig for grubs and insects. Snakes have been killed by them; the armadillo uses the hard edge of its carapace to cut them.

like the jaguar have a large enough gape to crack its protective shell.

All over their range armadillos have been relished for their flesh and the armour can be fashioned into a basket with the tail bent under and inserted into the mouth to make the handle. As yet this persecution has had little effect on the armadillo populations.

In its movement up into the USA, the nine-banded armadillo is increasingly meeting the hazard of motor traffic. This danger is accentuated because of the animal's habit of leaping into the air if alarmed, so that even when straddled by the wheels of a fast-moving vehicle, the upward jump of alarm results in the armadillo crashing against the chassis.

Some species of armadillo are agricultural pests, tearing up crops in search of insects, but they are also beneficial because they eat unwanted insects. The rather rare fairy armadillo is becoming rarer because increased ploughing, due to the spread of arable land, disturbs its way of life.

Resurgent armadillos

The armadillo family shows all the signs of being in decline. Its range is restricted to tropical and subtropical America. The living species are few and specialised in habit, being limited to running and digging. There are no climbers or swimmers. The largest living species, the giant armadillo, is dwarfed by the fossil *Glyptodon* that stood 5 ft high. If no more, this suggests a dying down in the adaptability in the race as a whole. The fairy armadillo, perhaps the most specialised, is also the most restricted. Its final stronghold in the sandy plains of Argentina is now being threatened by expanding agriculture.

Although the armadillos seem to be declining, and everything points to this, one species is actively extending its range. This is the nine-banded armadillo. In 1880 it lived little farther north than the Lower Rio Grande Valley on the borders of the United States and Mexico. By 1905 it had moved into the western half of Texas as far as the Colorado River. Since then it has moved into Louisiana, Florida and Mississippi. It has occasionally been found in New Mexico and Oklahoma but frosts have prevented it from becoming firmly established.

Why this sudden burst of life should have occurred is not known. There is little sign that the nine-banded armadillo is enjoying especial freedom from enemies, abundance of food or a rapid rate of breeding. Rather the reverse is true. Usually a zoological group, like an individual, reaches a peak of development, then declines. There are, however, one or two examples from the fossil record suggesting that groups may take on a new lease of life.

◁ *Small bony plates form the basis of the armadillo's armour (natural size).*

made up of small plates of bone, each covered by a layer of horny skin and separated from its neighbours by soft skin from which sparse hairs grow. The carapace, or back armour, hangs down over the body protecting the soft underparts and limbs. It is divided into two shields, one covering the fore limbs and one the hind limbs, the two being linked across the middle of the back by a series of transverse bands of plates that allow the carapace to be flexed. The number of transverse bands varies between species, and in some they are sufficiently flexible to allow the animal to curl up. The head is also armoured and in most species the tail is protected by a series of transverse bony rings. The softer underparts are covered with a dense layer of hair and scattered small bony scales.

If cornered armadillos will defend themselves with their sharp claws, but they are more likely to run away, some species moving surprisingly fast. They will also attempt to burrow into the ground if they cannot find a hole. Armadillos like the pichi will draw in their feet and wedge the surrounding carapace firmly into the ground This ruse is effective against birds and some mammals, but not against coyotes who can pierce their armour. The three-banded armadillo is more effectively protected by its complete rolling up but large predators

Armadillos -
▨ Nine-Banded
(Dasypus novemcinctus)
▨ Giant
(Priodontes giganteus)
▤ Fairy
(Chlamyphorus truncatus)

Armadillos -
▨ Central American Five-Toed
(Cabassous centralis)
▦ Brazilian Three-Banded
(Tolypeutes tricinctus)
▨ La Plata Three-Banded
(Tolypeutes matacus)

class	**Mammalia**
order	**Edentata**
family	**Dasypodidae**
genera	***Chaetophractus*** *hairy armadillo* ***Dasypus*** *nine-banded armadillo* ***Chlamyphorus*** *pichiciego and others*

John Markham

Armoured catfishes Corydoras aneus *members of the mailed catfish family* Callichthyidae, *resting on some pebbles using their pelvic fins as support. This family is identified by the clear arrangement of two rows of armour plates along the sides of the body. The 'whiskers' or barbels give catfishes their name.*

Armoured catfish

There are more than 50 species of armoured catfishes and all live in the streams of South America. They are small, the largest being less than 1 ft long, and they are remarkable for two things. One is their bony armour. The other is the method of fertilisation used in most of the species. They belong to three separate families, the first of which, with only five species, is known as the thorny catfishes. The second, known as the mailed catfishes, have a smooth armour of two rows of overlapping bony plates on each side of the body. The third family, which has no common name and is consequently spoken of as the Loricariid catfishes, has the whole body covered with overlapping scales. All have barbels, the 'whiskers' which give catfishes their name.

Talking habits

Mailed catfishes often travel overland for considerable distances, pulling themselves along with the strong spines on the breast or pectoral fins and using intestinal respiration, like that in the thorny catfishes. Both have a supplementary breathing system, in which air is swallowed and the oxygen from it taken up by a network of fine capillary blood vessels in the wall of the intestine. One species of thorny catfish is known to aquarists as the talking catfish because both in water and when taken out it may make a grunting sound which is caused by movements of the spines in the pectoral fins, amplified by the gas-filled swim-bladder acting as a resonator. Several other catfishes also make these sounds.

Carnivorous feeders

Mailed catfishes live in small groups in slow-flowing streams, rarely in standing water, and they feed on small animals, such as water fleas. The thorny catfishes are active mainly at twilight, when they grub on the bottom for worms and insect larvae. Both feed on small pieces of carrion.

The Loricariid catfishes are bottom dwellers, mainly in mountain streams or swiftly flowing streams in the lowlands, and they have thick lips forming a sucker-like mouth by which they cling to stones and water plants. This serves two purposes: to maintain position against a strong current and, while doing so, to feed by scraping small algae from the surfaces of the stones and plants with their bilobed or spoon-shaped teeth.

Spawning with the mouth

Little is known about the breeding of the thorny catfishes, and although they have been kept in captivity by aquarists, none has been seen breeding. One of the mailed catfishes, known as the hassar, will spawn in captivity only when water is sprayed onto the surface of the water in the aquarium, simulating a tropical shower. There is some disagreement about which of two methods of mating is used by the mailed catfishes. Some observers say that the male grips the barbels of the female with his strong pectoral fins, so that the two lie with their underside apposed. In this position the male pours out his milt as the eggs are extruded, so fertilising them. The second method that has been described is the one in which the female takes the milt direct from the male into her mouth. There is a certain amount of ritual courtship beforehand in which the male nudges the female with his snout and then the two break off, swim over to the surface of a stone and clean it by removing the minute growths of weed and debris with their mouths. The nudging and the cleaning alternate so that by the time pairing takes place they are in a highly excited state and there are several clean surfaces. The purpose of the female sucking in the milt now becomes clear. She is able to swim the short distance over to one of the clean surfaces. There, the milt streams

to extrude his milt while the female fans with her fins drawing a current of water from him to her, bringing the milt washing over the eggs, so fertilising them. The strength of the current is increased by the female breathing more strongly than usual, which means that she opens and closes her mouth more vigorously, drawing water in and driving it out across the gills. The total result is to create a current which travels from her mate to herself and forms a whirl-pool over the place where the eggs are being laid, so that the eggs are bathed by a concentrated suspension of milt in water. After 9 to 12 days the eggs are ready to hatch. The male, who has meanwhile kept guard, frees the baby fishes from the eggs. He does this by alternately sucking up the spawn with his mouth and squirting it out and fanning it with his fins, until the membranes break and the babies can escape from the eggs.

animal in the world today, the armour and armament seem to be out of all proportion, as if evolution had run amok in this particular species. One writer has suggested that a larger fish attempting to eat it would receive a sensation of having bitten a chestnut burr. The first item in this elaborate armour is the very bony skull, which is continued backwards as a bony plate overlapping the backbone, almost to the base of the dorsal fin. This fish, like other catfishes, has no scales. Instead there is a row of bony plates along each side of the body, and each of these plates bears thorn-like spines. All the fins are armed with spines, as is usual in so many other fishes, but a special feature of the talking fish is the large size of the pectoral fins. Each is relatively long and strongly constructed, and armed with strongly toothed spines. It has been suggested that, should the talking fish clasp an enemy with one of these fins, holding it against the saw-

◁ *Very rare striped sailback* Panaque nigro-lineatus *a Loricariid catfish, comes from Venezuela and Ecuador.*

▽ *Mailed catfishes out of water can pull themselves along on their pelvic fins breathing by swallowing air.*

out across her gills to the exterior as she breathes and the current of water carries it over the eggs as she deposits them on the cleaned surface, where they adhere.

As many as 250 eggs may be laid at one spawning and there may be more than a dozen spawnings during the course of a week, with several spawning periods during the year. The young hatch in 5 to 8 days. Some mailed catfishes make bubble nests. They rise to the surface to take in air, then release it from the mouth, in the form of saliva bubbles, under a roof formed by an overhanging rock or the underside of a waterlily leaf. The eggs are then laid among the bubbles.

The courtship of the Loricariid catfishes is more elaborate. For several days the couple clean a spawning site, and then the female takes up position in the middle of this site ready to lay. The male positions himself parallel to her, with his underside towards her, stretches himself so that both tail and head point upwards, the whole body forming a curve. In this position he begins

'Touch-me-not fish'

Nothing is known of the natural enemies of these fishes, but presumably they fall victim to the usual predatory fish and water birds. Mention of enemies, however, raises the point about heavy armouring, and recalls that one writer has spoken of the talking catfish as the 'touch-me-not fish'.

The most heavily armoured animal

It is usually assumed that animals wearing some form of armour enjoy protection from enemies as a consequence. This is only half true. The real situation is that, as an animal evolves armour, either enemies find a new method of attacking them, or other enemies arise capable of dealing with the armour. It is the same in human warfare. As soon as warships became armour-clad, an armour-piercing shell was invented. Similarly the invention of the tank was quickly followed by the anti-tank gun. In the talking fish, the most heavily armoured

like rows of spines on the plates covering the flank, the enemy would suffer severe lacerations. The trouble with this theory is that nobody seems to have seen the fish using its armament in this way.

The suggestion is in fact most improbable, and it is more likely that this is an instance in which a structure is evolved serving no very great purpose. The toothed spines on the fins, and the thorn-like spines on the plates of the flanks, may or may not have a value in protecting the fish. But when we look inside and see that the bones of the shoulder girdle are also toothed, we can say with certainty that this is something that just happened, and cannot conceivably have any defensive value for the fish.

class	**Pisces**
order	**Siluriformes**
families	**Doradidae** *thorny catfishes* **Callichthyidae** *mailed catfishes* **Loricariidae**

John Tashjian at Steinhart Aquarium

Jane Burton: Photo Res.

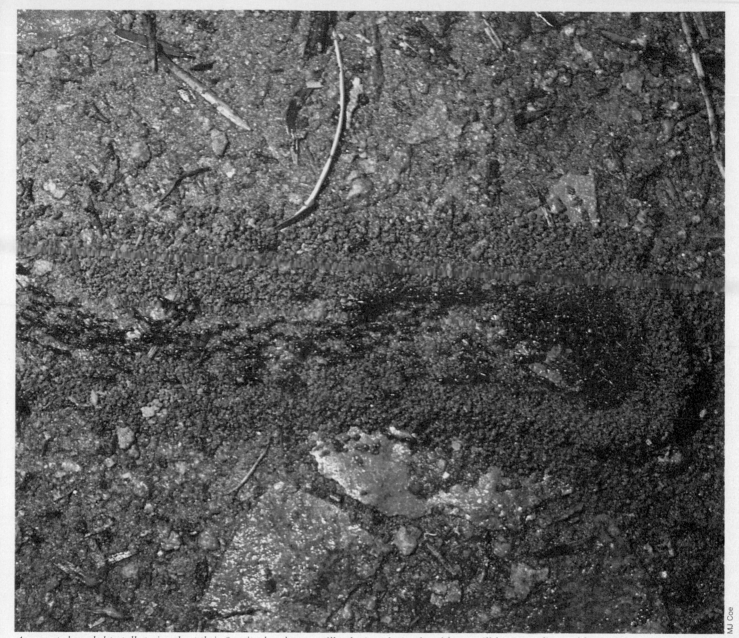

Army ants have led to tall stories about their ferocity, but they are still to be feared. A tethered horse will be eaten alive and left a skeleton.

MJ Coe

Army ant

Army ants, or driver or legionary ants, as they are also called, are often very large, more than an inch long. There is often so much difference between male, female and worker that early naturalists sometimes classified each as separate species, usually as a result of the insects having been found separately or away from the main colony. The queens are wingless. The males, by contrast, are winged and distinctly wasp-like in appearance, and there may be more than one kind of worker, showing marked differences, some being very large with powerful jaws and acting the part of soldiers or skirmishers. Although colonies may have vast numbers of individuals, there are relatively few species and genera. The main groups are the Driver Ants of Africa, and the Army Ants (Eciton) *from South America.*

Advancing columns drive all before

Army ants are confined mainly to tropical regions in India, Africa and South America, although in America they are found as far north as the Mississippi Valley and as far south as Patagonia. Unlike the complicated, settled existence of more familiar ants, army ants are nomadic, continually moving about the forests. They have no permanent nest and they are constantly scouring large areas in more or less regular columns, driving every living thing, large and small, headlong before them. The column may be many yards long, one writer telling of one in Nicaragua which he followed for several hundred yards without finding the end. In some places warning of the ants' approach may be given by birds that prey on them, for example antbirds or by the buzz of parasitic flies which lay their eggs in prey carried by the columns of ants.

The sight of a colony of army ants on the march is surely one of the great wonders of nature, and the resemblance of such a column to a human army is striking. In addition to the main body of small workers, larger, huge-jawed workers flank the main columns and continually scout ahead, laying scent trails to mark the way for the main body. Quite often, the press of the column is so great that new columns may split off, so that any slow-moving prey is often surrounded and engulfed. The activity of the column alternates equally between foraging, usually at night or on dull days, and resting, the nest being moved every day. Some species of army ants are averse to light and build long tunnels as they march, the main body of ants keeping out of sight within them. This does not slow them down, because the tunnels are built so rapidly that both the rate and secrecy of advance are maintained.

Victims eaten alive

While feeding mainly on other insects, little or nothing that is too slow to escape or insufficiently protected is safe from the attacks of army ants once they are on the march. Slow-moving animals often fall victim, such as snakes that are gorged with food and so will not move quickly. Even man will not always escape unscathed if he is foolish enough to let his curiosity or bravado mislead him into thinking the ants would not dare attack him. There are many stories of the intrepid white hunter's adventures with army ants, although these often grossly exaggerate the ants' intelligence and ferocity. Sometimes, in fleeing from the advance of the ants, it has been impossible to rescue horses or other livestock, and these if unable to flee themselves rarely survive. A tethered horse will simply be eaten alive and left a skeleton. A horde of African army ants was once seen to eat 3 dead goats in 3 days.

Despite their terrible depredations, however, army ants often perform a service to man by ridding his dwellings of vermin. Rats, mice, spiders, cockroaches, bugs, beetles, none survives an invasion of army ants and when the owners return again their houses will be free of these unwelcome squatters. It occasionally happens, however, that the marching column arrives while the owners are still asleep. Hundreds of ants crawl over you within seconds. In Africa a widespread belief is that driver ants do not attack until they have swarmed all over your body, and then bite all at once at a given signal!

Army ants feed by simply cutting up and rending the victim on the spot, carrying the pieces back to the temporary nest and also filling their crops with juice and pulp. Very large amounts of food are needed by an army ant colony. It has been estimated that in an average-sized colony of some 80,000 adults and perhaps 30,000 larvae, half a gallon of animal food is needed for its daily subsistence. With such great quantities of food needed, it is not surprising that army ants are only in the lush tropics.

25,000 eggs in 2 days every 30 days
It is said that the sole reason for the army ants' constant restlessness is that they are always exhausting the food in one area, and so must move to another place. But this is only part of the story. Even when food is plentiful, army ants never settle for long. The pattern of their movements depends largely on the breeding cycle. Every 30—40 days, the huge queen produces a vast quantity of eggs, perhaps some 25—35 thousand in 2 days. Several days earlier, the colony stops and gathers in a vast swarm, individual ants being held together by their hooked legs, the spaces between them forming rough and ready chambers for the queen and her forthcoming brood. The swarm may form in a hollow tree, hang from a branch, or simply lie in a cavity in the ground.

After the eggs are hatched, the community remains static, while the workers get food for the larvae. Fragments of food are handed direct to the larvae and not regurgitated in the form of a mush as in more advanced ant communities.

About a week later, the pupal cocoons, in which the previous generation of larvae have been carried, hatch almost simultaneously, producing workers and males. It is the movement of the newly-emerging ants

△ *The soldier ants are twice the size of the workers and have large heads.*
▽ *Army ants swarming from a branch, individuals being held together by their hooked legs. The spaces are used by the queen and her brood.*

which excites the older ants into beginning another cycle of nomadism. This is apparently further encouraged by the larvae of the new generation which exude a secretion when licked and cleaned by the workers.

After breaking camp, the ant colony, now supplemented by vast numbers of newly-emerged workers, march and forage, carrying the young larvae and queen with them. Each night, or during the day in the dry season, they swarm to form the characteristic temporary living shelters where the larvae and queen are protected.

When the queen is ready to produce a further batch of eggs, which usually coincides with the pupation of the earlier batch of larvae, the whole community stops once more, so the crucial parts of the life cycle coincide from one generation to another, reducing the time the army is stationary. Winged males are continually leaving to seek out queens in other colonies. Sometimes it seems they pick up the trails of other army ant colonies while on the march, and, leaving the colony of their birth, follow

them, but the exact means by which they find a queen is unknown. Male army ants are often quite enormous insects, with wings, large compound eyes, tremendous sickle-shaped jaws, and large abdomen and genitalia. In West Africa, where they are often found flying around lights, they are known as 'sausage flies'.

When daughter queens emerge in a colony, it may split up, each of the females gathering around her a proportion of the population and then going their different ways. In some species, however, most of the newly-emerging queens are killed, and only one queen is found in one colony, which may number up to a million individual ants.

Regimented ants

Reports of army ants on the march, the regular columns, the division into 'rank and file' with 'officer' types flanking the main body have frequently led the more romantic writers into crediting ants with far greater intelligence than they really deserve. In fact, the apparent regulated orderliness and 'intelligence' displayed by army ants are the result of pure instinct—the fixed behaviour patterns they have evolved. The vast majority of the colony are blind and are governed by an instinct merely to follow the ant in front, the column being guided by the soldier ants who precede the main column laying down scent trails. Yet even they are hardly seeking a path. Although best fitted to act as scouts and skirmishers, by reason of their size and armour, they take up their flanking positions merely because, being giants compared with the smaller workers, they are unable to find a footing amid the close-knit ranks of their brethren.

So it is a case of the blind leading the blind. Food is found by smell, and if there are any obstacles to the line of march, the ants have to search blindly for a way round. If a circular obstacle is placed in the centre of a colony of army ants, they will troop endlessly around it. Something similar has been seen to happen naturally. In Panama a column once became separated from the main army, described a circle by accidentally latching onto the end of its own column, and kept on marching round until the ants became weaker and weaker and eventually died.

The flanking and engulfing movements often observed in army ants are also more or less accidental in that because of the continual bustle and thrust of the main body, side-streams of new ant columns are continually being pushed out, these having the useful effect of surrounding and engulfing prey. The result of the formation of such side-streams may frequently be vast swarms of ants many yards wide: a terrifying prospect for man and beast alike.

class	**Insecta**
order	**Hymenoptera**
family	**Dorylinae**
genera	**Eciton** (South America) **Dorylus, Anomma** (Africa) and others

△ *A winged male known locally as sausage fly. For years they were thought to be wasps.*

▽ *Safari army ants marching in column. Large, huge-jawed workers flank the main column and scout ahead, laying scent trails to mark the way for the main body of army ants.*

Above: Arrow-poison frog.

Right: Arrow-poison frog Dendrobates leucomelas. *The poison secreted by these amphibians is so strong it kills very rapidly. Their bright colours give other animals warning of their poisonous nature so they are not eaten.*

Arrow-poison frog

Arrow-poison frogs are found only in Central and South America where the Indians have long extracted poison from their bodies for use on arrow-heads. Many amphibians have at least a trace of poison in their bodies or secrete poison from glands in the skin, and quite a few can cause a good deal of pain to any human that handles them. Only the arrow-poison frogs and one or two others secrete such a strong poison as to cause rapid death.

Most arrow-poison frogs can be distinguished by the nail-like plate on each toe. Many species are brilliantly coloured. The two-toned arrow-poison frog is brick red with patches of blue-black on its legs. More brilliant is the three-striped arrow-poison frog, which is yellow with stripes of black running lengthways down the head and body and around the limbs. Some species have 'flash colours' which are suddenly exposed as the frog jumps. It is thought that the bright colours, especially the 'flash colours' are warnings to other animals that they are not fit to eat.

A Cuban member of the family, Sminthillus limbatus is the smallest frog in the world, measuring less than $\frac{1}{2}$ in.

Habits

The various species of arrow-poison frogs are found in forests of different parts of Central and South America, some living in trees, others living on the forest floor.

Feeding

Arrow-poison frogs conform to the usual amphibian diet. As adults all amphibians are carnivorous. They take insects or other small invertebrates which are full of protein to restore worn-out tissue, and salts, fats, vitamins, and water needed for their metabolism. They also need carbohydrates which can be rebuilt from surplus protein.

Father carries the babies

There are several peculiar features about the breeding habits of arrow-poison frogs. Courtship or courtship rituals are rare amongst frogs and toads, but the golden arrow-poison frogs, and probably other species, 'play' together for as much as two or three hours. They repeatedly jump at each other, sometimes landing on one another's backs, as if fighting. Following the 'play', the eggs are laid, but there is no 'amplexus', the process in which the male, as in the common frog, perches on the female's back and fertilises the eggs as they are laid. The female arrow-poison frog lays her eggs on the ground and the male, who has been waiting nearby, comes over and fertilises them.

The absence of amplexus may be linked with the occurrence of the courtship play, because in frogs using amplexus it is often the pressure of the male hugging the female that causes the eggs to be extruded. When there is no amplexus, it may be necessary for another stimulus, in this case leaping about with the male, to initiate egg-laying.

Both methods ensure that there is a male present to fertilise the eggs which is the primary purpose of animal courtship.

When the eggs have been fertilised, the male carries them on his back where they become attached to his skin although how this is done remains to be discovered. After they hatch, the tadpoles remain on their father's back, getting no moisture except from rain. Up to twenty tadpoles can be found on one arrow-poison frog, and, as they grow, their father has to seek larger and larger holes in which to rest. Eventually he takes them down to the water and they swim away to lead an independent life.

Predator deterrent

Snakes, predatory birds and some carnivorous mammals will often prey on the majority of frogs. The arrow-poison frogs, however, possess the ultimate deterrent of the animal world—their flash colours give a warning to the predator, not to attempt to eat them because of their poisonous nature, giving the frogs a much safer life in their hazardous jungle existence.

Poison arrows into laboratory ploughshares

The Indians of South America are renowned for their use of poisoned-tipped arrows, which are reputed to cause death if they do no more than scratch the skin of their target. The best known of the poisons is curare, which is extracted from certain plants, but even this is a mild poison compared with that of the arrow-poison frogs.

The Indians collect the poison by piercing the frog with a sharp stick, and holding it over a fire. The heat of the fire forces the poison through the skin where it collects in droplets. These are scraped off into a jar. The amount collected from each frog, and its potency, varies with the species. The kokoi frog of Colombia secretes the most powerful poison known. This is a substance called batrachotoxin which has recently been shown to be ten times more powerful than tetrodotoxin, the poison of the Japanese puffer fish which had previously held the record as the most powerful known animal venom. 1/100,000 oz. of batrachotoxin is sufficient to kill a man.

One kokoi frog, only 1 in. long, can supply enough venom to make 50 lethal arrows. But the arrow-poison frogs are now being sought for more peaceful purposes. In the same way as curare has become an important drug because of its muscle-relaxing properties, so the venom of arrow-poison frogs is now being used in the laboratory for studies on the nervous system. It has been found that it acts in the same way as the hormones secreted by the adrenal gland, blocking the transmission of messages between nerves and muscles. Large amounts rapidly cause death, but in tiny doses it could well have medicinal value.

class	**Amphibia**	
order	**Salientia**	
family	**Dendrobatidae**	
genera	*Sminthillus*	
	Dendrobates, Phyllobates	

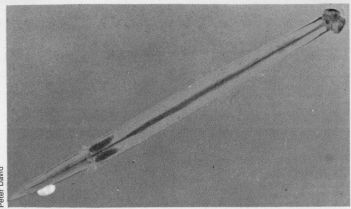

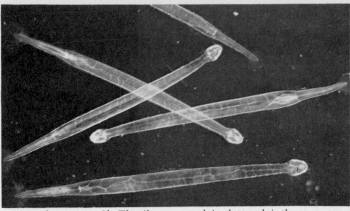

Arrow worm's body is divided into head, long trunk and tail. A jaw-hook and spines can be seen on the head; and two ovaries, full of eggs.

Sagitta elegans × 3½. *The silvery network in the trunk is the nervous system. Millions drift passively with the currents in the sea's plankton.*

Arrow worm

Among the myriads of tiny animals that float in the sea and are known as plankton, there are some with narrow, transparent bodies ¾ in. – 4 in. long. These are the arrow worms. At certain times of the year a tow net will catch vast quantities of them, but, when one looks down into the water, they will be very difficult to see. Their bodies are transparent, save for a pair of minute black eyes on the head, and can be seen readily only with food inside them.

When taken into the laboratory and coloured with special dyes, an arrow worm's body can be seen to have three sections: a short head, a long trunk comprising most of the body and a short tail. Arrow worms swim by up-and-down movements of the trunk and tail, aided by fins on the side of the body. Sagitta, the common arrow worm around the British Isles, has two pairs of fins on the trunk and a single, paddle-like fin on the tail.

The mouth is surrounded by a thin hood covering two sickle-shaped hooks that serve as jaws. On the hooks and around the mouth there are sharp spines which are used for capturing food when the hood is drawn back to expose them.

Throughout the oceans

Almost any bucketful of sea water will contain arrow worms. Most species live near the surface of the open seas but others live around the shores or at great depths, where they may be a beautiful golden-orange. They can swim by flexing their bodies but they cannot travel far on their own accord. Usually they hang passively in the water drifting with the currents.

Although the ocean appears to be the same in any part of the world, parts of it are as different as jungles and deserts on land. Throughout the ocean, the temperature and salt concentrations vary, and the distribution of the different animals varies with them, each animal being restricted to areas where conditions suit it. This is not strictly true for all marine animals, as the common mauve jellyfish *Aurelia* is world-wide, but it is true for arrow worms.

Arrow worms often migrate vertically, from the surface layers to deeper water and back. This is a habit of many planktonic animals and it is thought that many of them swim down to get away from too bright a light during the day. Arrow worms sink during the day and night, coming to the surface at dawn and dusk so that they are always in the most suitable dim light intensity.

Voracious feeders

Arrow worms are voracious creatures. They hang motionless in the water and dart at their prey, propelled by rapid flicks of the body. In a flash, they cover distances several times their own length, an unusual turn of speed for a planktonic animal, many of whom can barely swim at all but merely drift about. The prey is grappled by the bristle-covered jaws and hauled into the mouth where a sticky secretion, from special cells in the lining of the mouth, at once immobilizes it by gumming up its legs. It also acts as a lubricant to ease the passage down the gut.

Any small animal is taken, including other arrow worms, while herring larvae larger than the arrow worm itself are eaten in large numbers, especially in January and February when just hatched.

Not all arrow worms chase their prey. *Spadella* from the shores of south-west England lives in pools, attached to rocks or seaweed by special suckers on its tail. As a small crustacean swims past its head the arrow worm strikes at it with its jaw, without releasing its hold on the rock. The prey is worked round by the spines until head or tail can be dragged into the mouth.

Breeding

Like many invertebrate animals, arrow worms are hermaphrodite, that is, each individual has both male and female reproductive organs. In arrow worms the ovaries lie in the trunk and the testes in the tail. Eggs of one individual are usually fertilised by sperms from another, but self-fertilisation occurs in some species. The eggs are released into the sea where they develop into larvae, that later change into adults. Correct water temperature during the breeding season appears to be important to many arrow worms. If the sea currents carry them too far north, into colder waters, they fail to breed and, instead, grow to twice their normal size.

Guide to ocean currents

If a plankton net is towed up the English Channel from the open Atlantic Ocean the arrow worm *Sagitta elegans* will be caught in large numbers, but, just as the ship nears Plymouth, it disappears, to be replaced by another species *Sagitta setosa*. The change is so abrupt that on one occasion a marine biologist was able to catch *elegans* from the bows of his ship and *setosa* from the stern. The two look very much alike but can easily be told apart because if dropped into weak formalin preservative *setosa* remains transparent while *elegans* becomes opaque. This is a great convenience to the biologists of the Marine Laboritories at Plymouth because they can instantly distinguish between water from the channel, called *setosa* water for convenience, and water upwelling from the Atlantic, *elegans* water.

To the man in the street it may appear a matter of little importance whether one kind of arrow worm is found in one part of the Channel and not another, but in fact this knowledge helped to account for an otherwise baffling problem. During the first part of this century, fishermen used to put out from Plymouth to catch herring that appeared in the Channel off Cornwall every winter. During the 1920's the herring gradually ceased coming up the Channel and in a short while no more herring boats were to be seen. The fishermen, deprived of a means of livelihood, were unable to say where the herring had gone. For some years at the Plymouth Marine Laboratory routine tow-nettings were made and samples of plankton were brought back to the laboratory and analysed. These showed that *Sagitta elegans* was gradually moving further up the Channel. This could mean only one thing: that oceanic water was coming in from the Atlantic across the fishing grounds. Herring are very sensitive to changes of temperature. It became clear that the loss of the herring fishery off the south coast of England was due to the herring being driven away by the shift in the water currents.

phylum	**Chaetognatha**
genus & species	*Sagitta setosa* *S. elegans*

Asp

The asp, aspic viper or June viper, closely related to the common adder is a member of the family Viperidae. This is not stating the obvious because there are snakes called vipers that do not belong, and are not true vipers. In colour the two are also rather similar, the ground colour of the asp being lighter, usually grey, grey-brown, coppery red or orange. The underparts are grey, dirty yellow or blackish, with a sulphur yellow or orange red patch under the tip of the tail. The upper part of the body is often marked with transverse dark brown or black bars, sometimes zig-zags, and occasionally there is an inverted V on the head.

Differences in size and colour are very much less marked than in the adder.

The neck of the asp is more slender than that of the adder and the species rarely attains a length of more than 2 ft, the largest on record being 2 ft 2½ in.

Immediate distinction between the adder and the asp can be made by looking closely at the head. The shields on the asp's head are small, and the iris of the eye is shiny yellow, as compared with the coppery-red of the adder. Furthermore, the tip of the asp's snout is turned up to make a small spike. This feature is more conspicuous in two related species, the long-nosed viper of southern Europe and Lataste's viper of Spain and north-west Africa.

Distribution and habits

The asp is common in many parts of Europe, generally farther south than the adder, but where the two overlap it is often difficult to decide to which species a specimen belongs. Hilly or low mountainous country is especially favoured, often at high levels. They have been recorded at 9,700 ft in the Alps. Their distribution is quite widespread throughout Europe as shown in the map overleaf.

The habitat of the asp is generally warmer and drier than that of the adder. It frequents rocks, waste land, hedges and scrub, rather than sandy heaths, like the adder. Each individual has a small home range of several square yards which it rarely leaves. Asps are active by day and night, retiring at irregular intervals to a hole in the earth or between rocks. In winter they hibernate,

Asp Vipera aspis *showing the tip of its snout turning up to make a small spike.*

sometimes several individuals coiling together in one hibernaculum.

The asp is a slow-moving snake, but it is aggressive and is more dangerous to man than the adder. Accidents are fairly common especially in the south of France where the animal is common, and bites have proved fatal. Nevertheless, even in the south of France, where there are probably more cases of snake bite than anywhere else in Europe, venomous snakes are not such a danger to the public as in tropical regions.

Carnivorous feeders
Small mammals such as mice and voles, young birds and lizards make up the bulk of the asp's food. The very young eat earthworms and insects.

Ritual breeding battles
Pairing takes place in April and May. Males indulge in a ritual battle, while the females watch. First, the males attempt to intimidate each other by rearing up in an S-shape, then, if neither retreats, they chase each other and try to coil round each other's bodies. They never attempt to bite and neither is ever harmed.

Asps are ovoviviparous, the eggs being retained in the mother's body until they are due to hatch. Sometimes the egg-membrane ruptures while still in the oviduct and the young are born alive. A female produces 4–18 young, measuring 7–8 in.

Cleopatra's asp

Asps are best known for being the kind of snake with which Cleopatra killed herself. Yet it is hardly likely that she would have used the asp *Vipera aspis* as this species does not live in Egypt. The reason for Cleopatra's snake being called an asp is that in past times the name was given to any kind of venomous snake, much in the same way as 'serpent' is used to describe any snake.

The drawback to a member of the viper family being employed for suicide is that, even when deliberately encouraged, their bites are not often fatal. What is more, the effects of viper venom are usually painful and messy. The venom of vipers is a systemic poison, which clots the blood and destroys the lining of the blood vessels. The venom of cobras, on the other hand, is a quick-acting poison that interferes with the action of nerves and muscles. Herpetologists, specialists in the study of reptiles, have argued that Cleopatra's asp was most likely to have been the Egyptian cobra, *Naja haje*. This snake has been known for a long time as being able to kill quickly and painlessly, and was often offered to political prisoners as an alternative to more painful and dishonourable ways of dying.

As final support to this argument, it is the Egyptian cobra that is depicted on the headdresses in ancient works of art.

Mansell Collection

△ *Cleopatra with row of snakes on top of headdress. Although the asp is usually said to be the snake with which Cleopatra killed herself, it was most likely to have been the Egyptian cobra, which kills painlessly and quickly.*
▷ *Viper skull showing wide gape and the curved front fangs through which the venom flows.*

Asp (*Vipera aspis*)

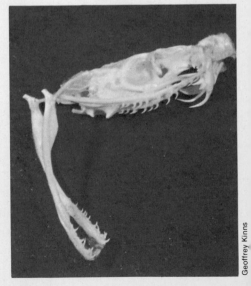

Geoffrey Kinns

class	**Reptilia**
order	**Serpentes**
family	**Viperidae**
genus & species	*Vipera aspis*

94

Ass

The name ass is given to two species of wild horse, Equus asinus of North and North-east Africa and Equus hemionus of Central Asia. Asses have been domesticated from early times, and the now extinct North African race of ass, Equus asinus asinus, probably gave rise to the donkey, referred to today as the domesticated ass. The word 'ass' for the domestic animal is mainly confined to the Bible.

Asses stand 3 — 4½ ft high at the shoulder with a grey or brownish coat, lighter on the muzzle, flanks and belly. The coarse mane lacks a forelock and the tail has a tuft of long hair at the tip. The legs are often striped like a zebra's. The ears are long.

It is doubtful whether there are any truly wild asses at large in Africa. Their numbers have been on the decline for centuries, the North African race becoming extinct in Roman times, and the others have interbred with domestic donkeys that have gone wild. The so-called wild asses found today in Ethiopia are probably derived from donkeys released by the Ethiopians as they retreated in front of the Italians during the last Abyssinian War.

The Asiatic wild ass is more numerous and is being protected in several parts of Asia. There are three races of Asiatic ass, which are probably all the same but have been given regional names: they are the Onager of Persia, the Kiang, Kulan or Chigetai of Mongolia and the Ghorkar of north-west India. Because of the protection schemes, the Asiatic ass is better known than the African, and it is the life-history of the former which is described.

Wary herds in the desert

Asses live in desert or semi-desert areas, sometimes on plains, but penetrating high into mountains. Hilly areas are preferred, but the asses come down into the valleys to avoid dust or snow storms. Soft sand is avoided as it makes travel difficult and food scarce. At one time the range of the Asiatic ass was considerable. In the seventeenth century it extended from the Black Sea in the west to the Yellow River of northern China in the east.

Very wary animals, wild asses cannot be approached easily, and they keep well away from human habitation even when suffering from thirst. Despite this, Russian biologists have been able to gain considerable information on their habits. The asses live in troops of 10 to 12 consisting of a stallion, several females and some juveniles. In autumn and winter, troops may band together into herds two or three hundred strong. Such a concentration is possible in the winter as it is then that the desert plants flourish. In summer, the population spreads out and waterholes become very important in determining the distribution of the troops. They never move more than seven or eight miles from water, whereas in winter, when the

△ Mule, the result when a female horse is crossed with a male ass. Beasts of burden since Greek and Roman times, they are very sturdy.

▽ 'Behold thy king cometh unto thee, meek, and sitting upon an ass, and a colt the foal of an ass.' St Matthew, chapter 21, verse 5.

J Allan Cash

Mansell Collection

95

vegetation becomes lush, they will move six times as far, as water is got from the grass.

The Russians also found that in spring the asses are active throughout the day, but as the weather gets warmer they take to lying up in thickets during the hottest part of the day and emerge to graze and drink at night, when the temperature has dropped and they can feed in comfort.

A food for each season
The diet varies throughout the year. In spring the main food is grasses and sedges, then as the vegetation begins to wither and the short-lived plants dry up, the asses turn to herbs such as tansy.

In the northern and mountainous parts of their range, asses may be seriously affected by snowfall. If it is much more than a foot deep they are severely hampered both in movement and in feeding and they have to browse on tamarisk and other bushes. The severe winters in 1879 and 1891 are thought to be the reason for the extinction of wild asses in Kazakhstan.

Breeding
The rut, or courtship, takes place during the spring or summer, the exact date varying from region to region. The stallions become very excited, racing round their troops, rolling on their backs and fighting each other before mating with the females. The foals are born eleven or twelve months later and the mares generally breed only once in two years, starting when two or three years old. A few months after foaling, some of the mares and their offspring are driven from the troop to be taken in charge by the younger, solitary stallions.

Stallion defends against enemies
Man has been the wild ass's main enemy, as its flesh and hide are much sought after by the inhabitants of desert areas. The introduction of firearms must have been a major factor in the decline of the ass, as wariness would no longer ensure its safety.

Apart from man, wolves are their principal enemy. A troop of asses has little to fear, but a solitary animal falls an easy prey.

If danger threatens, the stallion leads the troop away, but will turn back to chivvy the females if they lag behind, nibbling them, neighing and shaking its head.

Ass × horse = mule or hinney
A species is defined, basically, as a group of animals that cannot breed with another group, but in all definitions there are exceptions. The most familiar exception to this is represented by the mule and the much rarer hinney. A mule is the offspring of a female horse and a male ass, while a hinney's parents are a female ass and a male horse. Both are sterile and cannot themselves breed, each individual having to be produced from a cross between the two parent species. The mule is very ass-like with its long ears, thin legs and small hooves, while the hinney is a small horse-like animal, less sturdy and less common than the mule.

Mules have been used as beasts of burden since Greek and Roman times, being extremely sturdy animals and, unlike a horse, able to recover quickly from being worked to the limits of their endurance. Their tougher hide makes them less liable

Okapia

to suffer from saddle-sores and chafing, while they are relatively insensitive to disease. This makes them ideal as pack and draught animals especially in desert and mountainous regions, where their ability to live on coarse herbage and very little water, rivals, if not exceeds, that of the camel. Although they have now been largely replaced by motor transport they are still used by armies operating in mountains.

The wisdom of the mule

Other attributes of the mule are their intelligence and their proverbial stubbornness. Mules were extensively used by the armies in World War I for driving transport wagons and light artillery. British soldiers who had to handle them spoke of them sardonically as their long-faced friends because, they said, nothing could equal the obstinacy of a mule. If a mule decided not to do something you had almost to wait for the animal to change its mind, because it would not be driven. However, a mule's obstinacy was not always blind, and there

was one occasion when a transport column was moving along a road, in the summer of 1918, when the British army was advancing rapidly on the Western Front. Suddenly the leading mules stopped dead and all the rest followed suit. Their drivers were unable to make them take another step. Then, a hundred yards or so ahead of the transport column, a battery of field guns opened fire. The mules went forward of their own volition as soon as the firing ceased. It transpired that the battery had pulled into position during the night, and was so well camouflaged that the drivers of the mules had no idea of its presence. Yet the mules must have heard the guns being loaded, and had no intention of being under the muzzles of the guns as they went off.

Small herd of grazing asses. They usually live in desert or semi-desert areas, sometimes on plains, but often penetrate high mountainous areas. The Nubian ass has been extinct for centuries and the Asiatic wild ass enjoys a much reduced range. At one time it extended from the Black Sea in the west to the Yellow River in China. They usually live in troops of 10–12 but in autumn and winter they may group together into herds of two hundred to three hundred.

class	**Mammalia**
order	**Perissodactyla**
family	**Equidae**
genus & species	*Equus hemionus* *E. asinus*

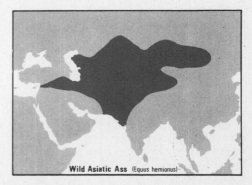

Wild Asiatic Ass (Equus hemionus)

97

Assassin-bug

Some 3,000 species of assassin bug have been described, and it is likely there are many more yet to be discovered. They vary in size, from a few millimetres to three or four centimetres, and in colour and structure. Some species are very thin and stick-like with elongated coxae (the basal parts of the legs), making them look rather like a mantis, while others are more solid and typically bug-like. Most species have two pairs of wings, although some exotic species are wingless. All assassin-bugs have a powerful, curved rostrum, or beak, with which they pierce and suck out the tissues of their prey.

Habits

Assassin bugs are so called because of the speed with which they grab and poison their chosen victim. They are common and widespread throughout most of the world, more particularly in tropical and subtropical areas. Only six species are found in Britain, often in buildings. They can be found on old walls, in houses or out-buildings, and even in thatch roofed cottages. The large *Reduvius personatus* is occasionally attracted to lights on warm evenings in late summer. Others are found on flowers, deciduous and coniferous trees, sand dunes, amongst piles of faggots, under stones, and even in old birds' nests.

Assassin-bugs often produce sounds when touched and this brings us to the first surprising use of the rostrum. When not feeding, the rostrum rests against a ridged groove under the head, called the prosternum. When disturbed the insect stridulates, scraping the one against the other, the friction producing the sound. It may be that this deters predators, such as birds.

Fearsome hunter

All assassin-bugs are carnivorous, and many of them are extremely active and efficient hunters, with a pair of powerful, jack-knife forelimbs for grasping the prey. On the end of these limbs there are adhesive pads made up of thousands of tiny hairs, covered by a thin film of oil. These adhere to the victim rather like a sticky burr. Some species have evolved even stickier pads, which enable the assassin-bug to hold fast even to the hairy body of a bee, in much the same way as a man might grasp a hedgehog between two large brushes.

Some assassin-bugs pursue their prey in a series of jerky runs, while others simply lie in wait for their victim, pouncing when it comes near enough. Others have evolved elaborate methods of enticing prey into their reach. A few species, for example, plunge their forelegs into the sticky resin exuded from pine trees and then hold them up to form alluring traps for other insects. A West Indian assassin-bug secretes fluid from its undersides which ants find very attractive. It intoxicates them so they fall easy victims to the bug.

Various assassin-bugs look very much like the insects on which they feed, so they can approach and seize their prey more easily. Some British species look like the gnats and midges that they feed on. They will also take bark-lice, attacking them through their protective web of silk. It is this that probably leads them to stealing insects shrouded in silk in spiders' webs.

Among other small creatures commonly eaten by different species of assassin-bugs are book-lice, gall-forming aphides, silverfish, flies, bed-bugs and harvestmen. These are all small insects harmful in some way to man. The huge African assassin-bug *Platymeris rhadamanthus,* is also a predator of the large rhinoceros beetle, a pest of coconut plantations, attacking this heavily armoured titan at its weak points by thrusting its beak through the joints between legs and body.

Like all carnivorous bugs, assassin-bugs feed by external digestion. They push their rostrum into the victim's body and inject into it a highly toxic fluid which acts especially on the nerves and muscles and then breaks down the body tissues. In most other bugs there is one channel in the rostrum for discharging the toxic saliva and another alongside it for sucking up the liquefied food, but assassin-bugs have one large tube that serves both purposes. With this larger tube a very large amount of digestive fluid can be rapidly injected into the victim's body, so prey many times the size of the assassin-bug can be quickly overcome.

The effects of the saliva are almost immediate. The amount injected probably varies according to the size of the victim, but a cockroach has been seen to die in 3 to 5 seconds, while the caterpillar of a moth, over 400 times the bug's weight, died in 10 seconds. When its prey is this size, the assassin-bug may live off it for days or even weeks, ignoring all passing prey. After such a feast, the bug may double its body weight.

Not all assassin-bugs feed on other insects or invertebrates. The tropical Triatominae attack mammals, birds and reptiles and suck their blood. One species is a nuisance at night, coming into bedrooms and attacking the occupants, while another's stab is said to feel like an electric shock.

Life history

The commonest British assassin-bug, *Coranus subapterus,* mates in the autumn. The eggs, which are dark brown in colour with a paler cap, are laid in crevices, amongst leaf litter and moss, and hatch the following April or May. The larvae, which apart from size differ little from their parents, are carnivorous from the start. They moult several times during the two months before they mature.

Reduvius personatus mates several times and egg-laying begins about a week after the first copulation. The female lays 3 to 5 eggs daily, the final total being usually between 50 and 150, laid between mid-June and September. The eggs hatch in about 20 days and the larvae immediately camouflage themselves against predators by assuming a covering of dust, repeating this procedure after each moult.

Assassin but not safe

While able to inflict sudden death on others, assassin-bugs are themselves preyed on by many enemies, especially birds and reptiles.

Many species, however, have a device which is often successful in repelling predators. The large, 1½ in. long *Platymeris*, for example, can use its paralysing venom as a liquid projectile, squirting a jet through its rostrum up to a distance of 1 ft with extreme accuracy. By rotating its head and depressing the curved rostrum slightly, it is even able to spit accurately over its 'shoulder' into a space above and behind it. Since as many as 15 jets can be fired successively, this can be a most effective deterrent. Certainly the effect of the saliva on humans is often extremely severe, as research workers studying these insects in laboratories have found. It can cause temporary blindness if received in the eye as well as severe irritation of the sensitive membranes in the nose.

Darwin's illness

It is said that the hall-mark of the true naturalist is that he or she should have a lively interest in, and affection for, all forms of life, however repulsive. If we accept this principle, then even the great Charles Darwin does not quite measure up to our highest ideals. In his *Journal of a Naturalist*, Darwin tells of the disgust he felt at being afflicted by South American assassin-bugs as they crawled over his body at night. Yet perhaps we should forgive his uncharitable thoughts for he had good reason for feeling repulsion, for it is one of these bugs, *Triatoma megista*, which transmits Chagas's Disease.

In later years Darwin suffered from a strange, incurable illness which was never diagnosed. The symptoms make it seem likely that his illness stemmed from his encounter with the assassin-bugs, which are known to carry trypanosomes, minute protistans that cause disease. Trypanosomes are the agents that are carried by tsetse-flies that cause sleeping sickness when injected into the bloodstream by the latter's bites.

class	**Insecta**
order	**Hemiptera**
sub-order	**Heteroptera**
family	**Reduviidae**

1 Assassin-bug Prithesancus brawni. *The long powerful jack-knife forelimbs are used for grasping prey.*

2 Close up of the head of Sirthena carinata. *The powerful, curved rostrum, or beak, is used to pierce the prey and discharge toxic saliva and then suck up the liquefied body tissue. When not in use the rostrum is tucked away under the head. This close up also shows clearly the compound eye with its many facets, typical of insects.*

3 Most bugs have two pairs of wings, but exotic species are often wingless as seen here in Fitchia aptera, *photographed at Lakehurst, New Jersey.*

Atlantic salmon

With a slim, streamlined body, the salmon is obviously built for speed, and this is confirmed by its long, leaping and powerful struggle when captured on rod and line. It is 40—50 in. long, exceptionally 60 in., with silver underside, flanks verging on green, and a silver-grey back. The flanks and back are covered with black spots. It is one of the family Salmonidae, which consists of only five genera, and perhaps two dozen species, including the familiar brown and rainbow trout. The salmon feeds in the sea and breeds in freshwater, a type of behaviour we call anadromous (from the Greek for running upwards). It is a matter of opinion whether the species was originally marine and took to migrating into rivers to spawn, or a freshwater fish that has taken to going down to the sea to feed. Most evidence is in favour of the former.

A thousand mile migration

Most of our knowledge of the habits of salmon concerns their stay in fresh water. Since this is part of the breeding migration, with no regular feeding, the details are given in the next section. What happens to salmon in the sea is still largely a closed book, although it has been a focus of interest for scientists for many years. Recent results from tagging experiments show that the salmon may travel up to a thousand miles or more from the river mouth where they enter the sea, although most of them wander less than a hundred miles from it. Since a salmon returns to spawn in the same river in which it was hatched, there has been a great deal of speculation and some research on how this is done. Some of the suggestions are; that the returning salmon is guided by currents, that it smells or tastes the water from its parental river and so is led to the source, that it uses celestial navigation to guide it, or that it can detect the varying salinities or the oxygen content of the water. Possibly all these are used in varying degrees at different stages of the journey. The one thing we can be sure of is that, once the salmon has entered its ancestral river, it has the urge to go up-stream no matter what the obstacles. So we have the famous leaps up waterfalls, 10 ft leaps being recorded. Where a river is dammed, as for an hydro-electric station, fish 'ladders' are often built, in the form of a series of steps, for the salmon to make their way upstream.

The upstream migrations from the sea may be in winter or early spring (spring fish) or summer to autumn (summer fish). When they run up-river, the salmon are in good condition, their flesh firm and red and the surface of the body silvery. There is much fat stored in the body but later, as a result of spawning, this is used up, the flesh becomes pale and watery, and the outside of the body loses its silvery appearance, becoming dark red. The skin of the back becomes thick and spongy, with the scales deeply embedded in it. Large black spots margined with white appear on the body, which is spotted and mottled with red and orange. This gives the 'red fish', which are males, the females being similarly coloured but darker, and known as 'black fish'. The males are further distinguished by the way the snout becomes longer and the lower jaw hooked.

Food into red flesh

During their stay in the sea, the salmon spend much of their time at moderate depths, which may account for the infrequency with which they are caught in trawls. They probably come nearer the surface at night, following the plankton on its daily migration upwards, since they feed on various shrimp-like crustaceans. It is from the pigments in these, especially the carotenoids, that the salmon's flesh derives its pink colour. In addition sand-eels, small herring and other fishes are taken. When in fresh water no regular feeding takes place, the salmon drawing on its reserve food store of fat.

Never safe from predators

Eels take the eggs, and many birds as well as perch, pike and trout feed on the young fish. Otters will take adults of quite considerable size. In the sea the main enemies are seals, porpoises and cormorants, perhaps also some of the larger predatory fishes.

From gravel stream to ocean deep

The Atlantic salmon breeds in the rivers of Europe, from Spain to the White Sea, off Iceland, the southern tip of Greenland, and North America, from Labrador to the New England coast.

The life-cycle begins in the shallows of a stream where the water is clean and there is a gravel bed. Spawning is from September to January, mainly in November and December. The ripe female digs a trough by lashing movements of her body and in this lays her eggs, the total numbers laid in a season being 800—900 for every pound of her weight. They are fertilised by the male in attendance on her, by shedding his milt over them, after which she covers the eggs with gravel and moves up-stream to repeat the process. The spawning ground is spoken of as a redd. The eggs are about 7 mm diameter. They hatch in 5—21 weeks, depending on the temperature.

The fry, when hatched, still carry a yolk-sac, are $\frac{1}{2}$ in. long and are called alevins. They remain among the pebbles of the redd until the yolk-sac is absorbed, in 4—8 weeks from hatching, then leave for shallow water when 1—2 in. long. They are then called fingerlings. At the end of a year, when 3—4 in. long, the fingerlings become parr, and by the end of the second year they reach a length of $4\frac{1}{2}$—8 in. At this stage

Mature male salmon in fine condition caught while returning to his ancestral breeding ground. By the time he reached the spawning ground the curved hook on the lower jaw would have become more elongated and grotesque.

Barry Driscoll

Mature salmon return from the sea to spawn in the same river where they were hatched. No matter what obstacles are encountered they will struggle onwards, leaping determinedly up waterfalls, until they reach their ancestral birthplace.

the body is marked with ten or eleven dark bands, like thumb-marks, on each side of the body.

The time at which the various stages are reached varies with temperature and other factors, including latitude. The discrepancies become even more pronounced in later stages, as when the parr becomes more silvery and, as a smolt, is ready to go to sea. At this stage it is not easy to distinguish it from a trout. In southern England, for example, the smolt stage may be reached in a year, while in northern Scandinavia, it may be seven or eight years before the parr becomes a smolt.

On reaching the sea, the salmon feeds for one to six years, before coming back to the same river to spawn. The returning salmon has been called a grilse, a name that has been given so many meanings that some authors have discarded it and prefer to speak of the returning salmon as a maiden, and then as a spawner when it reaches the spawning grounds. After spawning, the spent salmon, or kelt, drop down river tail-first, weakened by fasting and spawning, often attacked by disease. Many, especially the males, die on the way. Those that reach the sea, the mended kelts as they are called, soon recover and start to feed. They are now 'once spawned sea-fish' and when they return once more to spawn they are referred to as 'bull trout'.

Salmon's tottering throne

Eating the King of Fish, the Atlantic salmon, is a luxury. Catching it provides sport for the well-to-do and profit for the poacher. Ten years ago five million pounds of salmon were marketed. Even farther back in British history apprentices were rebelling at being given salmon to eat more than twice a week. Now it has disappeared completely from rivers where it was once plentiful, the result of pollution by factory effluents. Other rivers are being poisoned by pesticides washed out of farmlands, and this is happening over the whole range of the species. In fact, it has been suggested that the salmon may be doomed to extinction.

On the northern seaboard of Spain are many rivers where salmon can still be caught. Elsewhere in the Iberian Peninsula, which for centuries produced fantastic numbers of this fish, salmon are gone. In the 11th century they were the prerogative of noble families and abbeys. In 1258 they were protected by royal edict. In the 18th century up to 10,000 salmon were caught in Spain every day. By 1949 only 3,000 salmon a year were being caught. Under rigid protection this has increased to 7,000 in 1968, but the rivers where salmon have been lost are not being replenished by natural or artificial means. The causes of this tremendous fall

in the numbers of salmon are illegal fishing leading to over-fishing, the damming of rivers for irrigation and pollution by waste from factories.

The disappearance of the bulk of French salmon dates from the Revolution. Before, they were conserved by the monarchy, nobles and church, for their own ends, it is true, but they were conserved. Following the Revolution they were anybody's fish. Even later, when laws were made for their protection, illegal fishing with nets, poaching with tridents, damming of streams for mills and, later, hydro-electric schemes, as well as pollution, helped the decline of salmon resources. A law of 1865 required anyone building a dam to put in a salmon ladder, for the fish to migrate upstream. It did not, however, lay down that sufficient water should be allowed to flow down the ladder to allow the salmon up, so the law was honoured in the breach.

The situation in the Baltic is mixed. The salmon has suffered drastically in some countries, notably Poland, but the fishery has actually improved in Norway. In Sweden the use of hatcheries has so improved remaining stocks in the Baltic itself that one in four of salmon caught are from these hatcheries. Such declines as there are may be due to illegal fishing, damming of rivers, industrial pollution and the netting of salmon at sea, when young as well as mature fish are netted.

In England and Wales where the salmon was once king, few salmon rivers remain. Typical is the River Thames, which once teemed with 'fat and sweet salmons' ascending the river to 65 miles above London. It is now barren, for most of its length a sewer of industrial and human waste. Elsewhere the story is much the same.

Salmon was the first fish to be mentioned in the chronicles of North America. Now it is referred to as 'the American disaster' in the annals of fishing. The story is much the same as for Europe, perhaps more intensified. Over-fishing, damming of rivers for mills, blockading of rivers for lumbering, pollution with sewage and industrial waste.

Two new factors cause even greater apprehension for the future. One result of the tagging of thousands of young and mature salmon is that the fishes are now being traced to their feeding grounds. These will certainly be in international waters, and there, as history shows, the chances of controlling over-fishing are slim. The second adverse factor is the cumulative pollution of all rivers, indeed all waters on the globe, with pesticides and other toxic residues.

Despite all that is now known we are still ignorant of many aspects of the salmon's biology, a better knowledge of which could help us prevent the disastrous demise of this useful food fish. The Atlantic Salmon Research Trust was set up in 1967 and if it can work quickly enough it may yet save the valuable and beautiful fish.

class	**Pisces**
order	**Salmoniformes**
family	**Salmonidae**
genus & species	*Salmo salar*

Leaping salmon

1 Atlas moth eggs 7½ × natural size

2 Newly emerged larva × 12.

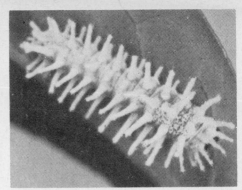
3 Second stage larva × 7½.

4 Third stage larva × 3.

5 Fourth stage larva × 1½.

Photo series by JA Wilson

6 Full grown larva—natural size.

Atlas moth

Probably the most famous of the large moths, the atlas moth belongs to the family Saturniidae which includes the British emperor moth, the North American cecropia moth and the tussah, or tussore, silk-moths of southern Asia, all of which produce a large silk cocoon, several having been used commercially.

The female is larger, heavier and more massive than the male, and her 'hooked' fore-wings may span ten inches. The general colour of body and wings is tawny but with a beautiful pattern, and there is a conspicuous triangular, transparent spot on each wing.

Habits and life-history

The atlas moth is found in the tropics and subtropics, from India, including the Himalayas, eastwards to Malaysia and Indonesia. The spherical eggs, about 2½ mm in diameter, are laid in clusters on a wide variety of tropical shrubs, including cinnamon and hibiscus. The larvae (caterpillars) are at first white but later turn a pale bluish-green. The body is ornamented with rows of spines and is covered with a white, waxy powder. Two, sometimes three months after the eggs are laid, the caterpillar, which is now 4–4½ in. long and over 1 in. in diameter, spins around itself a tough, papery cocoon of silk in which it pupates. This cocoon is attached to the foliage of the food-plant. It has no opening and the moth gets out in the same way as other cocoon-spinning insects, by secreting a liquid from the mouth parts which dissolves the silk and enables the moth to push its way out.

This moth can be kept in captivity in temperate latitudes, feeding readily on privet, willow or rhododendron, but a temperature of 21–26°C/70–80°F needs to be provided.

The largest in the world

Atlas, in Greek mythology, was one of the Titans, therefore a giant. The atlas moth is sometimes named as the biggest moth in the world, but in New Guinea and Australia lives the hercules moth—named after another giant of mythology. Its wings are less than 10 in. across but broad and ample, giving a total surface area of nearly 100 square inches, probably making it, by a short head the largest of all moths. Another candidate for the title is the great owlet moth of South America, which has the widest span, its long, narrow wings measuring up to 12 in., but it is less heavily built than the other two.

At the other end of the scale is the midget spotkin, a leaf-boring moth, which is just over 1/12 in. across.

Some of the smallest insects of all are beetles known as feather-winged beetles (family Trichopterygidae) living in tropical America and Australia. The smallest of these is ¼ mm long. There is, however, a family of parasitic wasps (family Mymaridae) known as fairy flies, that lay their eggs in the eggs of other insects. The smallest of these is the smallest known insect and is only 0·21 mm long. This means that there are some insects that are smaller than the largest single-celled animals (the Protozoa) and are truly microscopic. By contrast the largest known insects are larger than the smallest vertebrates. The Luzon goby, a fish found in the Philippines, is less than ½ in. long when fully grown, so is much smaller than many insects.

phylum	**Arthropoda**
class	**Insecta**
order	**Lepidoptera**
family	**Saturniidae**
genus & species	***Attacus atlas***

7 *Cocoon dissected to show pupa* × ¾.   8 *Adult female—underside* × ½.

9 *Adult female altas moth* × ⅞.

The world's giant.
Hercules moth Coscinoscera hercules has
unquestionably the largest wing area of
any insect. Although the wings do not
reach the 10 in. width of the atlas moth,
they are broad and ample, giving a total
area of nearly 100 sq. in.

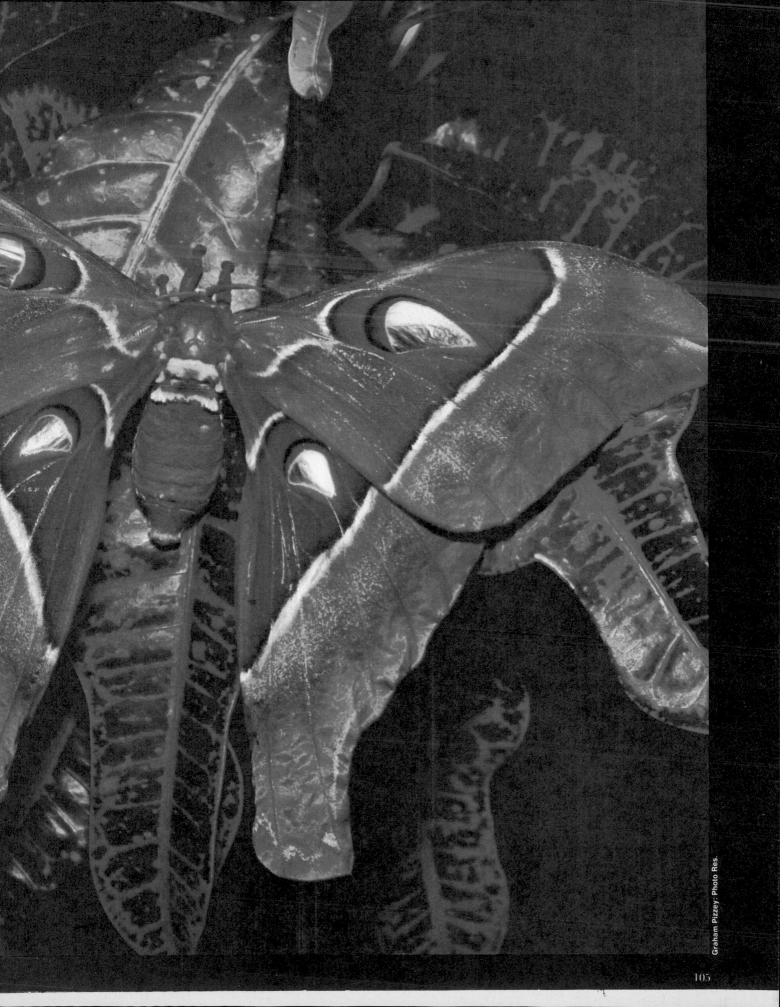

105

Avadavat

There is only one species, with three races of avadavat: the Indian or Bombay avadavat, the Javan avadavat and the golden-bellied avadavat of Burma. The name 'avadavat' is a corruption of Ahmadabad, the Indian city from which the birds were first sent to Europe. The Javan race is sometimes called the 'strawberry finch' by bird fanciers, but the name is not restricted to this race. Other names for the species are tiger finch or red waxbill. Avadavats are about the size of wrens but are strikingly coloured. The male is coppery to bright red with black underparts, dark brown wings and tail, and reddish-brown crown. The back, rump, wings and belly are dashed with white spots. The female is more sombre, being dark brown with paler underparts, yellow on the belly, having some red on the tail and rump, and white spots on the wings. The male avadavat is unique in the finch family for having a non-breeding 'eclipse' plumage: at the end of the breeding season the male moults to a plumage very much like that of the female, although he can always be distinguished from her by the brighter and more extensive red on his rump.

Clumping birds

Avadavats live in damp areas where reeds and tall grasses flourish. Well known as cage birds, they do well in captivity. They can be left outside in mild winters, but it is wise not to let the cage temperature drop below 7°C/45°F.

When they are not feeding or busy with nesting, avadavats spend their time sitting together in small groups, usually of three or four, and sometimes up to nine. Like the anis, the avadavats are very tolerant of each other's company and they do more than merely sit together. They actively 'clump'. That is, they push or lean against each other, so much so that a bird on the outside may have to lower its wing as a prop, to prevent itself from being pushed over. Clumps usually start to form around a bird that is sitting quietly. Other birds approach it carefully in a submissive attitude. Normally, when one animal approaches another that is not already its mate or its companion, that one will show aggression. A show of submission calms its fears so that it is not provoked into attacking or fleeing.

Bright birds feed right

In the wild, avadavats feed on the ground, picking up seeds and insects. In aviaries the selection of food for avadavats is very important, for if they are not well-fed, they lose the brilliant red plumage and become coppery brown or even black. A recommended diet is seed, such as small yellow millet, fresh seeding or flowering grasses, ants and their pupae or 'ants' eggs'.

All these foodstuffs contain carotenoids, members of the group of chemicals to which carotene—which gives the orange colour

Avadavat, favourite of bird-fanciers, is named after Ahmadabad, the Indian city.

Zool. Soc. London

to carrots—belongs. The birds convert these chemicals into brighter forms, which become concentrated in their feathers. Once a week, and more often in winter, the seed is treated with halibut oil, and crushed eggshell and sand given.

Post-monsoon breeding display

In the wild breeding takes place after the monsoons. Before mating the avadavats go through a series of displays. One is called the straw display in which either the male or the female picks up a feather or piece of grass by the shaft and, holding it out in front of itself, fluffs out its feathers and bows slowly. The displaying bird, be it male or female, also sings during the display, a high-pitched warble which slowly descends the scale.

Each male defends an area extending several yards in each direction from his nest. Somewhere in this area will be a special perch where he sings.

He shows fight to any male that comes into his territory, by displaying at him or actually attacking. The signal that releases a cock's aggressiveness is the red plumage on the other cock. This acts in the same way as the red breast of the robin. Females and cocks in eclipse plumage are ignored. Hens, however, will attack other hens.

The nest is untidy, not neatly woven like those of the related weaver finches. The avadavats take bundles of material to the site, usually high in a tree. First, a flat platform is made amongst twigs, then grass is added and finally a lining of feathers.

Four to six pure white eggs are laid and incubated for about 29 days. The young are fed by both parents. When a young avadavat is approached by one of its parents it crouches and opens its bill, at the same time waving its head, unlike the other nestlings of its order, which merely stretch their necks and gape. It also opens both its wings and often flutters them. This performance is known as food-begging and the form it takes depends on how hungry the chick is. If it is well fed the chick merely opens its bill without begging.

Social preening

Avadavats, and other birds that live together in close groups, can often be seen preening each other. This is called allopreening, to distinguish it from autopreening, when a bird preens its own

feathers. In allopreening, the preening bird grasps a feather of the other bird at the base and draws its beak along the shaft gently nibbling at it as it goes. This is precisely what a bird does when preening its own feathers. Allopreening is, however, usually confined to the partner's head, and the bird being preened assists the preener by rolling and twisting its head to present different parts to the preener's bill.

Allopreening takes place when the avadavats are perching in their tight 'clumps'. Sometimes a bird will lean over its neighbour and preen the bird beyond it. A more careful watch on the 'clump' will show that a bird invites another to preen it by adopting a special 'invitation' posture. It ruffles the plumage around its head and rapidly opens and shuts its beak, sometimes uttering a very high-pitched, rapidly repeated call. If very keen to be preened, it will even push against the bird it is inviting and repeatedly bring the top of its head in front of the latter's bill.

At first sight it would seem that allopreening enables a bird to get its head preened, an action it cannot perform itself. This idea was tested by putting flour onto the head feathers of some avadavats, but there was no difference in the time spent being allopreened before and after soiling, so allopreening must serve some other function. Further observations showed that allopreening is used to reduce aggression between two birds, for whenever two animals come together they will either be aggressive or fearful of each other. In a 'clump' the head of an avadavat is exposed, and this is the part that is likely to be attacked by another bird. The ruffling of the head feathers in the invitation posture can therefore be construed as a gesture of appeasement, turning the bird's mood from aggression to a friendly preening. Further allopreening will help cement the friendly relationship. It is very likely that allopreening started as a means of getting inaccessible parts of the body cleaned, but it now has an added, more important function. Birds will spend much more time allopreening than is necessary for cleaning the feathers, confirming its social function of ensuring group harmony.

class	**Aves**
order	**Passeriformes**
family	**Estrildidae**
genus & species	*Estrilda amandava*

Avadavat (Estrilda amandava)

Avocet

Waders belonging to the family Recurvirostridae, avocets are immediately identifiable by their long, upward curved beaks. There are four species widely distributed.

The plumage of the Old World avocet is a striking pattern of black and white, which in fact acts as camouflage. Immature birds have a brown tinge.

The American avocet is slightly larger, with a yellowish-brown head and neck. The Chilean and Australian avocets are very similar in colouring, the Chilean is darker above than the American and the Australian avocet's plumage is a reddish-brown. The latter has crossed to New Zealand several times but has never become established there.

Habits and habitat

The black and white beauty of the graceful avocet is so strikingly impressive that it has been adopted as a symbol by the Royal Society for the Protection of Birds. Avocets are shore-birds, with the exception of the Chilean avocet that lives in the high Andes. They breed on mud flats, lagoons and salt marshes around the coast, and sometimes in less saline areas. Outside the breeding season, sandbanks and shoals, or flats around lakes and rivers are a favourite haunt.

In flight, the neck is only slightly extended so that it looks comparatively short. The legs are held out, extending well beyond the tail. Wingbeats are rapid and regular until landing, when the bird glides in. After landing it frequently stands for a short time with wings extended.

Avocets may be seen singly, but they are gregarious birds, often being seen in flocks of up to 20—30.

The call note is a musical, flute-like 'klooit', also being used as an alarm call, when it is uttered more rapidly.

Sweeping for food

The feeding patterns of waders depend on their bill shape. Many of them use their long bill to probe the mud and sand along the margins of the seas in search of the small animals that live beneath the surface. The curved bill of avocets is an adaptation to a slightly different food source. They live on small crustaceans, fishes and molluscs, as well as seeds and other plant material, that float around the shore. They wade through the shallows with the bill held just below the water, the front end parallel to the surface. In this position the birds move forwards, sweeping the bill from side to side through a 50° arc.

It is obvious that a bird with a straight bill would not be able to feed like this. Every now and then the avocets raise their bills to swallow the food that has been caught in the slightly opened beak. In deeper water the head is held under water and they may 'up end' like a duck.

Avocets often feed in groups, striding forward shoulder to shoulder, and up to 300 have been seen feeding together.

Eric Hosking

△ *Old World avocet displaying aggressively while standing over its eggs. The black and white striking coloration serves to break up the body outline, helping to conceal the bird. This is known as disruptive coloration.*

▽ *Young avocets hatch in May after about 23 days' incubation. They will swim and catch food within a few hours and become independent at 10 weeks. As they nest on the ground they are extremely vulnerable to rats and man.*

Eric Hosking

Black and white beauty

1 *Avocet in flight.*

2 *The curved bill of the avocet is held just below the surface of the water and parallel to the surface. The bird moves forwards, sweeping the bill from side to side, capturing small crustaceans, fishes and molluscs.*

3 *A breeding pair of avocets fighting off an intruding male. In waders, gulls and related species both members of a pair will attack an intruder, whereas in the smaller birds it is usually the male only that defends the territory.*

Eric Hosking

Breeding behaviour

The Old World avocet breeds around the North Sea and Baltic coasts (and formerly in Ireland) also around the Mediterranean, Caspian and Black Seas, and in the northern provinces of China south to Iraq and Baluchistan.

Avocets nest in small colonies in which their relatively small nests are sometimes only 2 ft apart. In sandy areas no nest material is used, but, when there is vegetation about, this is used in nest building. The colonies are often subject to sudden flooding, when the avocets rush round collecting material so as to raise the eggs clear of the water.

As happens in several animal species, amiable enough at ordinary times, the avocets become savage when breeding. The breeding pair (it is impossible to tell the difference between the sexes) will attack and chase away any other avocet who dares to intrude.

Mating is accompanied by an elaborate ceremony and nearly always takes place in the water. The female crouches low in the water, while the male walks backwards and forwards behind her, preening himself continuously, perhaps as a sign of nervousness or indecision. Gradually he draws closer until he brushes against the female's tail and eventually he jumps on her back. After mating the male jumps to one side of the female, opens his wings and the pair run together with one of the male's wings held over the female's back.

Between 2 and 8 eggs, usually 4, are laid in late April or early May. Both parents share in the 22—24 day incubation periods. The chicks fend for themselves, leave the nest soon after hatching, swim and catch food when a few hours old and are independent at 10 weeks.

Enemies and defence

Avocets have been extremely vulnerable to man and rats, and other animals that can take advantage of a ground nesting bird. This vulnerability, together with the draining of the marshes, has led to the avocet's disappearance from many parts of its former range.

In common with many other waders, avocets often show very little fear of man, refusing to move far from their nests when flushed. More likely, they will fly out towards a human intruder and swoop over

his head in an effort to frighten him away from the nest. They will also perform distraction displays to lure an enemy away. The 'broken wing' display is typical. The bird lurches over the ground with one wing flapping helplessly, at the same time uttering plaintive cries. In doing this it makes itself very conspicuous to any predator who will probably be distracted from the camouflaged eggs and young and set out after an apparently more accessible, and bigger prey. The displaying bird deliberately leads the predator away from the eggs or chicks, then suddenly flies off as the predator draws near.

A success for conservation

At one time avocets bred in England from the Humber to Sussex, but destruction of the habitat by draining and indiscriminate killing led to a decrease in their numbers, until the last recorded nesting, in Kent, in 1842. For nearly a century they were only seen as migrants, then two nests were found in Ireland in 1938. Next, eight pairs bred in Suffolk in 1947. Suitable conditions for breeding were created by the war, when

much of the coast was put out of bounds and many marshes were flooded. Four of these pairs bred at Minsmere and four at Havergate Island. A band of local birdwatchers was immediately formed to guard them and Havergate Island was bought by the Royal Society for the Protection of Birds. The next year five pairs bred at Havergate. While there has been little success at Minsmere and at other places, sometimes because of nest robbing, the Havergate colony has flourished. By 1967 108 pairs were there. It is highly probable that these colonists came from the large colonies in Holland, only 100 miles across the sea to the east.

Communal dancing

During the early part of the breeding season, when the avocets are still forming pairs, elaborate ceremonies take place apparently to strengthen the bonds between the pairs. Groups of avocets gather on a sandbank or other open space and bow, their long bills pointing towards the ground. Sometimes such a group arranges

Photos by Pamela Harrison

Hazel Earle

itself in a circle with the birds facing inwards and bowing towards each other.

During the performance the avocets appear to be under considerable stress as they perform rather uncourtship-like actions. The bowing may alternate with bouts of head-shaking or peeking at the water or sideways sweeping of the bill as they do when feeding. Such movements are the same as those we perform under stress, such as scratching the head, doodling or drumming the table. We do these when perplexed or in an awkward situation, not knowing which course of action to take. They are called 'displacement activities' and occur when an animal is faced with two conflicting lines of action. For instance, on meeting a rival, an animal has the choice of attacking or fleeing. If it is not sure which to do, it may do neither and, instead, do something completely unexpected like preening itself. This is then called 'displacement preening', and is similar to a man scratching his head while wondering which way a job should be done.

Sometimes the avocets' gathering will lead to actual fighting, in which the pairs try to keep side by side. In attempting to attack another, an avocet will edge towards its opponent with legs bent, and try to slap it with its wing. Often they leap up so that they can beat down at each other or avoid the other's blows.

Even in these fights there is tension in the birds, for in the middle of an encounter, one will suddenly sit down or place its head behind its wing. This 'sleeping' is a good example of a displacement activity.

class	**Aves**
order	**Charadriiformes**
family	**Recurvirostridae**
genus & species	***Recurvirostra avosetta*** *Old World avocet*
	R. americana *American avocet*
	R. novae-hollandiae *Australian avocet*
	R. andina *Chilean avocet*

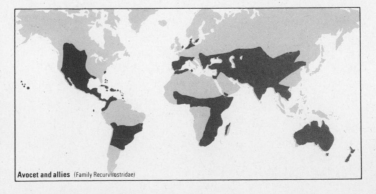

Avocet and allies (Family Recurvirostridae)

The distribution of the avocet family is world wide. Included in the family are the four avocet species, the stilts and the ibisbill.

109

Axis deer

The most common deer in India is one of two species of axis deer, known as the chital (the Hindustani name) and those who know it well claim it is the most beautiful deer in the world. Usually the beauty of a species of deer depends on the fine head of antlers the stags can attain. The beauty of the chital lies in its coat, which is bright reddish-brown with lines of conspicuous white spots, set off by the white underparts and the insides of the ears. The antlers are slender and have few branches, or tines, compared with the red deer or the wapiti. The chital, also known as the spotted deer, is unusual in that the stags shed their

Habits and habitat

There is no segregation of the sexes, as in many deer, except perhaps that stags leave the herd when their antlers are about to be shed. Otherwise the chital lives in herds of up to several hundreds, including stags, hinds and young of varying ages. The habitat may be lowland plains or the lower hills, among bushes or trees or in bamboo forests, especially near a stream, with a ravine for shelter. The axis deer swims well and takes readily to water.

Browsers and grazers

Less nocturnal than most deer, the axis feeds for 4 hours after sunrise, then goes to water, rests in shade in midday heat, and feeds for a couple of hours before sunset. It is both a grazer (grass-eater) and a browser (eater of leaves).

of how these predators benefit the prey species by preventing the destruction of the habitat.

Deer readily increase in numbers if not checked. For example, axis deer were introduced to the Andaman Islands. They flourished and soon became a pest, moving out from their wild habitat into cultivated land. To check this two leopards were introduced — but care was taken to select two females, for fear that with a rich supply of food a pair of leopards would quickly breed, and lay the foundations of a worse pest.

Cruelty to deer?

In a sophisticated society any suggestion of cruelty to animals is repugnant to an important section of the public. Consequently, there tends to be adverse reaction to any

Roy A Harris & KR Duff

Axis deer Axis axis. Often called the chital (the Hindustani name) or the spotted deer. Although often found in herds of several hundreds, axis deer do not overgraze the habitat as predators such as the wild dog and the leopard keep them on the move.

Chital Deer (Axis axis)

The axis deer or chital lives in a variety of habitats feeding by day as well as by night.

Introduced into Ceylon

Hog Deer (Axis porcinus)

The hog deer skulks usually in open plains in its range. It is rarely found in herds.

antlers at all times of the year and the fawns can be born at all times. Their body-size varies from one area of the range to another. In northern and central India the chital stands up to 3 ft at the shoulder, in southern India it seldom exceeds 2½ ft.

There is another deer living alone, or in parties of up to 18, on the grassy plains of northern India and Burma, and in some parts of Ceylon. It is known as the hog deer for its squat, pig-like appearance and movements. Its legs are short, its body smaller and stouter than that of the chital, and it runs head down, not bounding like other deer. Yet it is an axis deer, a close relative of the chital, in spite of its being so different. Its coat, for example, is brown with a yellowish or reddish tinge, and has a speckled appearance, because some of the hairs have white tips. Also, the antlers are small and set on long bony stalks or pedicels. But its young are spotted and, surprisingly, it readily interbreeds with the chital.

Enemies prevent overbreeding

Mating takes place mainly in winter in northern India but fawns can be seen at all times of the year, born 210–238 days after mating.

Axis deer were once indifferent to the presence of human beings and, because they do not run away from man, in some parts of their range they have been severely reduced in numbers or even wiped out. In other areas their numbers have increased because natural enemies, for example, leopards, have been shot. The enemies are of two kinds: those, like the python, that take a small but steady toll of the numbers, and those, like the wild dog and the leopard, that not only prevent excessive increases in numbers but also keep the herds on the move, so that no part of the habitat is overgrazed. In countries other than India, especially those into which deer have been introduced as park deer and have then gone wild, we hear a great deal today about the need for culling (organised killing of a certain number) to prevent deer destroying their own habitat. This is because of an absence, in their new habitat, of natural predators. The axis deer is a good example

suggestion of culling deer. EP Gee, the well-known naturalist, ardent conservationist, and authority on Indian animals, has spoken wisely on one aspect of this problem. He relates cruelty to the way deer react to their enemies. Does a deer live in continual terror of being hunted or killed? Probably no wild animal feels any more apprehension of danger or death than we do in crossing a busy street. The chances of death are as great, or almost as great, as for deer in the wild state. We know there is danger. We are alert to the possibility. We are not actively apprehensive. So with deer in a wild habitat, they are ever alert to danger, with keen senses to detect it, and instinctive and instantaneous reactions to minimise it. One result is that it is mainly the weak and the sick that are caught by natural enemies.

class	**Mammalia**
order	**Artiodactyla**
family	**Cervidae**
genus & species	***Axis axis** axis deer or Chital **A. porcinus** hog deer*

Albino axolotl Siredon mexicanum. *Externally it seems to be a juvenile, but internally it is a sexually mature adult. For years zoologists were unable to decide where axolotls fitted, until they were observed changing into adult salamanders.*

Axolotl

The axolotl is the Peter Pan of the amphibian world, being able to reproduce its own kind while still in its aquatic larval stage. This is unlike the usual development of amphibians such as the common frog, toads and newts, which as larvae, or tadpoles, are confined to fresh water. In the adult form they can live in water and on land, reproducing in water in the breeding season. Certain amphibians, the Mexican axolotl being the most famous, are able to complete their life cycle without ever leaving the water, as sexual maturity is reached in the larval stage.

The axolotl is a newt-like creature, 4—7 in. long, usually black, or dark brown with black spots, but albinos are quite common. The legs and feet are small and weak, while the tail is long, with a fin running from the back of the head to the tail and along the underside of the tail. It breathes through the three pairs of feathery gills on the sides of the head.

Habits and habitat

Axolotls are quite often kept in aquaria, especially in schools. This is rather surprising as they are rather dull animals, spending most of their time at the bottom of the tank, occasionally swimming about lazily for a few seconds before sinking again. A probable reason is that the axolotl can reproduce its own kind without ever leaving the water. Newts and most salamanders, kept in captivity, need water, land and very careful keeping if they are to survive and breed successfully.

Axolotls cannot be kept together with complete safety as they are liable to bite off each other's gills and feet, and bite pieces out of the tail. If this does happen, however, and they are then separated, the missing pieces will regenerate.

In the wild, axolotls are confined to certain lakes around Mexico City, where they are regarded as delicacies when roasted. The name axolotl is Mexican for 'water sport'.

Zoologists were unable to decide where to place axolotls in the classification of amphibians, until 1865 when, at the Jardin des Plantes in Paris, the problem was solved. Several specimens had bred successfully, when one day it was noticed that the young of one brood had lost their gills and tails, and had quite a different coloration. They had, in fact, turned into salamanders. This was the secret of the axolotl. It is one of several species of salamander, an amphibian which normally has an aquatic tadpole resembling the axolotl, that normally changes straight into the adult. The axolotl, however, usually becomes sexually mature while still a larva. This is because the axolotl fails to metamorphose (see overleaf).

Pre-packed sperm

In most frogs and toads, fertilisation of the eggs takes place externally. In other words, the female sheds the eggs into the water and the male simply releases his sperm near them, to make their own way to the eggs. The axolotls, related salamanders, and newts have a system of internal fertilisation but it is different from the normal method in which the male introduces the sperm into the female's body to meet the eggs waiting there. Instead, the male axolotl sheds his sperm in a packet called a spermatophore. It sinks to the bottom and the female settles over it and picks it up with her cloaca.

The male attracts the female by a courtship dance, secreting a chemical from glands in his abdomen and swishing his tail, presumably to spread the chemical until a female detects it and swims towards him.

About a week later, 200—600 eggs are laid, in April or May. They are sticky, and the female attaches them to plants with her back legs. The young axolotls hatch out a fortnight to three weeks later, depending on the temperature of the water. At this stage they are only about ½ in. long and remain on the plant where the eggs are laid. After a week they start swimming in search of food and, if the water is warm and food plentiful, they will be 5—7 in. long by winter. They will then hibernate, taking no food, if the water temperature drops below 10°C/50°F.

Carnivorous feeders

The youngest axolotls feed on plankton, minute organisms that float in water. Later they eat water fleas such as daphnia, and when fully grown they hunt for worms, tadpoles, insect larvae, crustaceans and wounded fish. Their prey has to move, however, and axolotls will ignore still, dead food given to them but will snap up a piece of food that is waved about in the water.

Precocious amphibians

The axolotl's habit of breeding while in the larval stage is known as neoteny, or the retention of juvenile characteristics in the adult form. By 'adult' is meant a sexually mature animal. This habit is not restricted to the axolotl. Other amphibians, including some salamanders, sometimes exhibit neoteny, failing to emerge onto land, but continuing to grow in the larval form.

The basic cause of neoteny seems to be a lack of thyroxine, the hormone secreted by the thyroid gland, which controls metabolism. If the secretion is upset in humans, several bodily disorders occur, including the formation of goitres, swellings in the neck caused by the thyroid gland enlarging. Administration of thyroid gland extracted from cattle, for instance, can often cure the goitre, and axolotls will change into adult salamanders if given thyroid gland.

It would seem, then, that there is something lacking in the diet of both axolotls, and humans with goitres. In Wyoming and the Rocky Mountain area the tiger salamander regularly exhibits neoteny and humans are liable to get goitres. This has been traced to a lack of iodine in the water, for iodine is an essential component of thyroxine. In these cases the administration of iodine, rather than thyroxine, is all that is needed either to effect the metamorphosis of an amphibian or cure a goitre. However, iodine treatment is not the only way of making axolotls metamorphose. Sometimes a consignment sent to a dealer or a laboratory will change into adults shortly after being received. Apparently, the jolting during travel has been sufficient to start the change.

When faced with an odd occurrence like this, a zoologist asks whether it confers any advantage on the animal. In the discussion on amphiuma it was seen that a freshwater animal has an advantage over a land animal

△ *It is now known that several species of salamanders are able to breed while still in gilled stage. The eastern mud salamander* Pseudotriton montanus *is one such amphibian.*

▽ *Adult of* Siredon mexicanum. *The axolotl in juvenile form can be made to change into an adult salamander by giving extract of thyroid, or sometimes a jolt will do it.*

because it does not have to conserve its body water. This could well be the reason for the axolotl's neoteny. The lakes where it lives do not dry up and there is an abundance of water, so it is an advantage to live and breed there, rather than risk life on the dry, barren land around. If the lakes dry up, then it can still change into a salamander, having the best of both worlds.

class:	**Amphibia**
order:	**Caudata**
family	**Ambystomidae**
genus & species	*Siredon mexicanum*

Jack Dermid: Photo Res.

Jane Burton: Photo Res.

The aye-aye's hand has a thumb like a man's and a flat nail on its big toe—primate features, relating it to monkeys and men. Its large eyes help it see at night as it creeps through the jungle, listening with its huge ears for grubs chewing wood beneath the bark. The long, narrow middle finger is used to extract grubs from holes made in the bark with the incisors (⅓ of natural size).

Malcolm McGregor

Aye-aye

Of all the strange, and unfortunately rare, animals that live in the forests of Madagascar, the aye-aye must surely be the strangest. Many of these rare animals are lemurs, to which the aye-aye is closely related. The size of a cat, with a bushy tail as long as its body, the aye-aye has a coat of thick, dark brown or black hair. The face is rounded, with large eyes and naked ears, erect, rather like those of a mouse. The fur around the face and throat is yellowish-white. The aye-aye could be described as almost squirrel-like, except for the bizarre hands and feet. Like those of other primates (lemurs, monkeys, apes) the hands and feet have opposable thumbs. Those of the hind feet have flat nails but all the other toes have pointed claws. The middle finger of each hand is extremely long and narrow, and is used for feeding and for combing the fur, for scratching and for picking the teeth.

Nocturnal habits
Aye-ayes live only in northwestern and eastern Madagascar where they inhabit forests, mangroves and bamboo thickets. Occasionally they are found in cultivated areas such as coconut plantations, but it is largely the clearing of the country for agriculture that has caused the aye-aye to become very rare. Where they have adapted themselves to life near human settlements they appear to be little disturbed by the general activity, motor transport, transistor radios and so on.

Man and the aye-aye rarely meet, as the aye-ayes are nocturnal, spending the day in a hollow tree or among branches. The Malagasy regard it with dread, as a mere touch from it is supposed to cause death. When irritated by man it is fearless, lashing out with its long, clawed fingers. Another legend credits aye-ayes as the reincarnated ancestors of the Malagasy.

Aye-ayes are mainly silent creatures, but they occasionally emit a short cry rather like pieces of metal being rubbed together.

Listening for food
Fruit, insect grubs, and possibly adult insects make up the aye-aye's diet. The two peculiar structures in their anatomy, the long middle finger and the rodent-like front teeth, are used for getting food. After nightfall an aye-aye creeps around the branches listening very carefully for the sound of an insect grub chewing its way through the wood. If it cannot hear anything, it delicately taps the branch with its long middle finger, listening, with all the skill of a piano tuner, for the change in sound that indicates a hollow where, perhaps, a grub is lurking. If an opening to the hollow can be found, the aye-aye will insert its long finger and try to hook the grub with its claw and haul it out. Failing this, the chisel-like front teeth are used to gnaw away the wood until the prey can be reached.

The front teeth are also used to pare away the hard wood of bamboos to get at the soft pith. Recently a French zoologist has described a pair of aye-ayes living in a coconut plantation. The ground was liberally scattered with half-eaten and abandoned coconuts. The aye-ayes came out in the evening and walked around the trees, each selecting a suitable nut. The incisors were used to sink a hole an inch or so in diameter into the side of the nut; then the middle finger was used to extract the milk and pulp, by poking it in the hole then licking off the adhering mush. Aye-ayes use the same trick for drinking water, sweeping it to the mouth at about 40 strokes a minute.

Breeding
The single young is born in a spherical nest about 20 in. in diameter with an opening in one side. It is built in a hollow tree or in the crotch of a branch. Apparently, the young are born in February and March. Nothing is known about mating, gestation period or whether the father stays with his family.

Conservation
In 1966 it was thought that less than a dozen aye-ayes were left in Madagascar, with prospects of extinction. Then the island of Noss Mangabé, just off Madagascar, was declared a reserve by the Malagasy Government, and nine aye-ayes were transferred to it. They appear to have settled down happily, but with a birth rate of one a year it will be some time before a viable population has built up.

An animal out on a limb
An important guide for the classification of mammals into their natural groups is the form of their teeth. For instance, the insectivores have sharp-pointed teeth suitable for crushing hard-bodied insects and the rodents have chisel-like front teeth suitable for gnawing. So when the aye-aye was discovered by a French explorer in 1780 he informed the scientific world that he had found a new species of squirrel (that is, a rodent). This was, in many ways, excusable. The aye-aye has long, chisel-like gnawing teeth (incisors) which, in true rodent fashion, grow continuously; there are no piercing (canine) teeth and the cheek teeth (molars) are flattened for chewing. It was not until its anatomy was fully studied that it was seen to be a primate. The opposable thumbs, the flat nail on the big toe, as well as a few characters of the skull, showed that it was definitely a primate, a relative of lemurs and monkeys. Even so it was a strange primate, having no really close relatives, even among the lemurs. Some of its features are very like those of extinct primates, so the aye-aye is the remaining, and now very withered, branch of a very old stock. In an evolutionary sense, no less than in its nightly wanderings, it is an animal out on a limb!

class	**Mammalia**
order	**Primates**
family	**Daubentonidae**
genus & species	***Daubentonia madagascariensis***

Babbler

A variety of birds are grouped together under the name 'babbler'. Some of them appear to bear little relationship to the others while a few can be fitted, only with difficulty, into the classification of birds. The 280 or so species of babblers are, accordingly, placed with the warblers, thrushes and flycatchers, which they most nearly resemble, within the large family Muscicapidae.

In general, babblers are poor fliers with short, rounded wings and fairly long tails. They live near the ground, searching for berries and insects. Some species are drab but others have brilliant markings. The smallest is the size of a wren, the largest the size of a crow. Their name comes from their continuous loud and varied calls.

The babblers are divided into six tribes: the jungle babblers, the scimitar babblers and wren babblers, the tit babblers, the song babblers, the wren-tit and its relatives, and the rock fowl, picathartes. Not all authorities agree that the last two should be classed as babblers, but there is no obvious other place for them.

A well-known member of the song babblers is the red-billed leiothrix or Pekin robin, as it is more popularly called. The Pekin robin is very much like a European robin in build, but slightly larger. Its plumage is olive green with red and yellow markings on wings and throat. The bright colours and an attractive song have made it popular as a cage bird. Despite its name the Pekin robin comes from the Himalayan region of India and southern China. The closely-related and slightly larger silver-eared mesia of the Himalayas and southeast Asia is also a cage bird. It is more brightly coloured than the Pekin robin, with a black head and silver-grey patches on the ears.

Life in dense forests

Babblers are mainly inhabitants of the Old World and are abundant in India, China and southeast Asia, extending to New Guinea, Australia and Africa, including Madagascar. The only American babbler is the wren-tit which lives on the Pacific coast from Oregon to Baja California.

The habits of babblers are very like those of the antbirds (see page 61) of the New World, living near the ground in dense forests, where they search for food in the undergrowth and the leaf litter. Although basically different in their anatomy, and bearing no relation to each other, the babblers and antbirds resemble each other in their weak flight and short rounded wings. This is an example of convergent evolution, where two unrelated groups of animals living in different parts of the world have both developed the same habits and have come to look very alike. The two main features of this convergence are probably linked with the similarity of the habitat; birds living in dense forests do not need powerful flight,

△ *There are nearly 300 species of babblers. The Pekin robin is one of the best known.*
▽ *The black chinned yuhina sometimes shares a nest between more than one pair.*

▽ *The rock fowl* Picarthartes gymnocephalus *was discovered over 100 years ago living in dense jungle in West Africa. It is such a curious bird that it was not classed as a babbler until 1951.*

indeed, the long wings, necessary for this, would be a disadvantage among dense foliage. Strong legs for walking or hopping in and out of the undergrowth are needed and both babblers and antbirds have these.

Outside the breeding season, babblers congregate in flocks, often of several species, which is another habit they share with antbirds.

When in their non-breeding flocks, babblers regularly form 'clumps', like the avadavat (see page 106), in which the birds huddle together on a perch. They also preen each other. This behaviour probably helps to keep the group together, as does their continual babbling song, which informs members of the flock where their fellows are while moving in dense forest.

Nest built of woven cobwebs

At the beginning of the breeding season certain flocks split up into pairs which spread out and take up territories, defending them against other pairs, or, in other species, pairs may remain together in parties throughout the breeding season. Nests are built near the ground and are well hidden by vegetation. Some species build open-cup nests while others build domed nests with entrances in the side. A feature of many nests is the delicacy of the materials used: lichens, spiders' webs and the skeletons of leaves.

The wren-tit's method of building the nest was studied in detail by an American ornithologist, and sheds light on how a bird can weave a stout, compact nest, firmly attached to a foundation of a forked branch or spray of twigs, with only its bill to manipulate the material. The wren-tits took a week to build their nests, which were made of bark fibre bound by cobwebs. First, a saucer-shaped network of cobwebs is woven between the twigs to form the foundation. Strands of web are then crisscrossed from twig to twig until a platform of considerable thickness is achieved, when bark fibres are also introduced. These are torn from old and weathered parts of stems, held in the bill and stripped backwards. When the platform is about an inch thick, the birds can sit on it while they work. Bark fibres are than placed around the rim and held in place by webs.

Spiders' web is ideal for nest material because it is sticky, so there is no difficulty in anchoring the ends. Similarly when pieces of web are placed together they stick, and the platform becomes a solid structure. The wren-tit holds the bark fibres in neat bundles in its bill when collecting them, so when these are placed on the rim of the nest they fall naturally into place. They are held by a mass of web placed on top, strands of which are teased out and anchored at various points so that the bark is strapped down. Finally, the loose ends of the bark are tucked in and secured with more web. When the nest bowl has been completed, it is lined with bark fibre and decorated on the outside with pieces of lichen.

Wren-tits raise one brood a year from a clutch of three to five eggs. The young leave the nest when 2 weeks old and start hopping around nearby twigs, learning to fly a little in another week. When 5–6 weeks old they can fly well and hunt for their own food and help their parents defend the territory.

In species where the flock stays together in the breeding season, communal breeding may take place. Little is known of the breeding habits of many babblers but some, including the silver-eared mesias, jay thrushes and yuhinas, have been seen to share a nest between more than one pair. Several birds may build a nest together and several females lay in it, while the young may be fed by any member of the group.

Collector's piece

One morning a strange bird was brought into the camp of Cecil Webb, who was collecting animals in the Cameroons for the London Zoo. It was a most unusual-looking bird with a bare, but brilliantly coloured head. Immediately Webb realised that he had a great rarity. It was a grey-necked picathartes or rock fowl. He was one of the few Europeans to have seen one alive, and he was even more lucky because this one had been caught in a spring trap designed to catch porcupines. Somehow it had escaped having its legs broken and the villager, who had caught it, intended to eat it but had brought it into the camp on the off chance that it might be wanted.

There are two species of picathartes, the grey-necked and the white-necked. They are the size of magpies and both have brilliantly-coloured bald heads. When they were first found at the beginning of the nineteenth century they were thought to belong to the crow family and were called bald crows. A century later they were moved to the starling family and only in 1951 was it suggested that they ought to be classed as babblers. Such uncertainty about the birds' relationships is not surprising, because they were known in Europe from only a few skins in museums. The grey-necked picathartes, in particular, has hardly ever been seen alive. When Webb tried to find out more about it, he learned that even the woodcutters working in the forest had never seen one, probably because the picathartes is even more an inhabitant of dense undergrowth than the other babblers. Strangely, it nests on rock faces, and these must be rare in the jungle. After a painstaking search Webb managed to find a small ravine with six large mud nests on the side of an overhanging face. These were the nests of picathartes. They were empty but they posed the problem of how a bird, more at home on the forest floor, could build its nest on a face more suited to a swallow.

Christina Loke: Photo Res

△ *Cobwebs are used to bind together the grass which makes the delicate nest of this yellow-eyed babbler. It is built near the ground and is well hidden by vegetation.*

▽ *This chestnut-capped babbling thrush from Malaya, feeding its young at the nest, shows its rounded form with short wings and tail suited to flitting through dense jungle.*

FGH Allen

class	**Aves**
order	**Passeriformes**
family	**Muscicapidae**
tribes	**Pellorneini** *jungle babblers*
	Pomatorhinini
	scimitar babblers & wren babblers
	Timaliini *tit babblers*
	Chamaeini *wren-tit and allies*
	Turdoidini *song babblers*
	Picathartini *rock fowl*

Baboon

There have been several studies in the last 20 years of apes, such as gorilla and chimpanzee, living in their natural homes. Instead of watching their behaviour in captivity, observers have kept a record of the apes' activities under natural conditions, perhaps spending years living alongside them. The results of these studies have greatly altered our views on the life of the apes and have given new insights into our own behaviour. Baboons have received considerable attention, one reason being that they often live in the open where they can be easily watched. These studies of baboons are important because they are of monkeys that have forsaken a life in the trees, and so may give us clues about how our ancestors made a similar move. Both must have faced the same problems of getting food and guarding against danger.

Baboons belong to the family of Old World monkeys. They inhabit most parts of Africa where they live in family groups, called troops. Smaller than chimpanzees and gorillas, they have long muzzles, and long tails, usually held in a characteristic inverted U.

Distribution and habitat

The chacma baboon lives in eastern and southern Africa, the yellow baboon in central Africa, the doguera baboon from Ethiopia to Kenya, and the Guinea baboon in west-central Africa. Gelada baboons, which are classified in a separate genus, are confined to the mountains of Ethiopia, while the hamadryas or sacred baboons are found farther north in Arabia, Egypt, the Sudan, Ethiopia and Somalia. They usually inhabit rocky open country or 'bush', but also live in woodland.

It is the social structure of baboons, the organisation of the troops, that has attracted the interest of psychologists. Each troop is a family unit with all mating taking place between the members of that group. Typically, the troop consists of old males, juveniles, females and babies. In a small troop there may be no more than one male with two or three females and their babies, but large troops may number up to 50. In addition, several troops may gang together to form herds.

The troop, as we have said, is a discreet unit—the members never wander far from each other and have a definite range of countryside over which they wander, searching for food. At first sight, a troop of baboons appears to have little order, but on observation, a definite social structure can be seen. This is most clearly seen when a troop moves into open country. In the van come some of the smaller males followed by females and juveniles. In the middle of the troop there are the females carrying babies, the young juveniles, and rather surprisingly perhaps, the old, dominant males. The rear is brought up by more females and young males. The advantage of this is that the females and young are

Andrew M Anderson: NHPA

116

◁ *Although baboons spend most of their life on the ground they are still quite at home in trees as man's ancestors must have been.*

▽ *This is a typical troop of baboons made up of one interbreeding family unit including an old male, juveniles, females and babies.*

Okapia

Zool Soc London

△ *A perfect example of aggressive expression in male gelada with upper lip pulled right back to expose vicious canine teeth.*

▽ *Open bush country is typical baboon habitat.*

Okapia

protected from all sides. Moreover, when danger threatens, the females and the very young start to flee first. The males move away more slowly, so they become congregated between the source of danger and the mothers and children.

A question that intrigued observers was how the troop kept together. It was known that in herds of antelopes, the males must constantly herd the members of their group to keep them together, but baboon families appeared to live amicably, the male having no need to force the others to stay with him. Nor were there many signs of violence between the males. Observations showed that, in contrast with the antelopes, other baboons would actively congregate round the males. One behavioural trait that assists in holding the troop together is mutual grooming. This is the mammalian equivalent of allopreening, seen in such birds as the avadavats (see page 106). When the troop is resting, or feeding quietly, they gather in small groups to groom each other's fur. This keeps the fur clean, but, more important, it promotes harmony between the individuals. The grooming clusters usually form around a dominant male but other clusters form when the baboons gather round a female with a newborn infant, which is apparently of great interest to them. Human beings are not the only ones to indulge in baby worship!

To what extent there is a stronger bond than this between the members of a troop, it is difficult to say. Certainly it is essential for them to keep together as a protection against enemies, but, according to some observers, if a baboon is sick or injured its fellows will show concern for it, ensuring that it is not left behind when the troop is on the move. However, other observers report that no such consideration is shown. Presumably the presence or absence of such compassionate behaviour depends on circumstances, such as the amount of danger. In a given area and in sight of one observer, this might be sufficient to cause a troop to flee with scant regard for the weaker members. He would then record that baboons act on the principle of 'the devil take the hindmost'. The age of the injured baboon may also be important. The cry of a young one when hurt, for example, will bring the adults running to its aid, as in people.

Lion and leopard main enemies

Spending the day in the open and sleeping at night in trees, as baboons do, is a sound basis for defence. The tactics of a troop when faced by a predator, as described above, are reinforced by a warning system. While moving about and feeding, the troop keeps up a chorus of quiet grunts, but any one of them, on being disturbed, will give a shrill bark to alert its fellows. If a female gives the alarm, one of the males will then move away from the troop to keep the intruder under observation and will give a double bark whenever it moves.

The enemies of the baboon are cats, principally lions and leopards. Cheetahs and serval cats may try to prey on baboons but with less success than the other two. The usual reaction to attack is for the baboons to make for trees or rocks where, safe from attack, they bark defiance, but

the old males are courageous and will sometimes turn on their enemies, several old males being more than a match for any of their predators, whether lion or leopard.

Breeding

Baboons breed throughout the year. When not pregnant or nursing, the females come on heat for a week in each month. Within the troop there is a hierarchy (or 'peck order') among the males, with little or no fighting. Moreover, all males are free to mate with receptive females, unlike many other animals, for example elephant seals, or deer, where the dominant male attempts to deny the other males access to the females. Pairings are temporary, the female mating with the young males when first in heat, and with the dominant males later.

The newborn baboon soon clings to the hair of its mother's chest. Within hours of its birth it must have a sufficient grip to hang on even when the mother is leaping into the trees for safety. As it grows older it learns to ride on the mother's back, jockey fashion, and soon after this it will begin eating solid foods and leaving the safety of its mother's body. Its excursions become more and more adventurous until it meets other young baboons, and starts to play with them. However, if danger threatens all run straight to their respective mothers.

The play group of young baboons becomes a very important factor in their life. It is here they learn the skills needed for later life, in the form of games such as chasing and mock-fighting.

Omnivorous feeders

Baboons eat a wide variety of foods, both plant and animal, depending on season, local availability, and the age of the baboon. For instance, some troops of baboons feeding in woodlands were seen to split up. Females with babies sat on the ground eating grass heads, while the juveniles and the young males climbed to the tops of trees to eat the leaves, bark and insects not available to the larger animals.

Seeds, shoots, tubers, buds and fruit are all eaten in season and grasshoppers, butterflies and lizards are caught. Scorpions are a delicacy—the baboons nip off the stings with their fingers. Hares may be flushed out of their forms and chased, several baboons joining in to catch them. Occasionally small monkeys, such as vervets, are caught, and skinned before being eaten. Newborn Thompson's gazelles, eggs and fledgling birds have been recorded as prey.

By tilling the soil, man has provided baboons with a plentiful supply of food, mainly in the form of fruit, and in many parts of Africa baboons have become a serious pest. Some of them develop a taste for milk, killing lambs and calves to get the milk in their stomachs.

A recent study by John Hurrell Crook showed that the troop structure of gelada baboons in Ethiopia depended to some extent on the amount of food available. Where there was an abundance of food the troops were large and contained many males, but in the arid areas a troop would have only one male. This meant that the females who needed a plentiful supply of

Beringer & Pampaluchi

△ *Baby baboon clings to mother for first few weeks but is soon more independent.*

△ *Hunted baboons bark defiance at their leopard enemy from the safety of a tree top.*

▽ *The first one which panics and tries to flee from the 'threatened' tree is certainly doomed.*

food for pregnancy and milk production, did not have to compete with males for the sparse supply. Yet the one male in the troop was sufficient to ensure procreation.

Jack the signalman

Before scientific studies on captive or wild monkeys and apes began, our knowledge of these animals was based more on anecdotes, casual stories about odd happenings. Even if these are not embellished to improve the story, anecdotes tend to give an over-estimate of apes' intelligence because they rarely deal with commonplace everyday events. One such story concerns a pet baboon belonging to a signalman in South Africa at the end of the last century. The Bushmen of South Africa claim that baboons can talk but take care not to let the white men hear them in case they are put to work. In fact this is precisely what did happen to the signalman's baboon, Jack. He learnt to perform several jobs for his crippled master who had a wooden leg. First, he learnt to put the little trolley his master used to get to the signal box, onto the rails, and then push his master to work. Then he learnt to operate the signal levers, even getting to know at which moment to work them. It was even claimed that he took the initiative, learning to do jobs by watching his master and performing them of his own accord. Perhaps the best story is one that shows his powers of reasoning. One day Jack had been up to some mischief and was about to be punished. He quickly snatched his master's stick and threw it away. A man with wooden legs in those days had no chance of chasing and chastising a baboon!

class	**Mammalia**
order	**Primates**
family	**Cercopithecidae**
genera & species	***Papio ursinus*** *chacma baboon* ***P. cynocephalus*** *yellow baboon* ***P. doguera*** *doguera baboon* ***P. hamadryas*** *sacred baboon* ***P. papio*** *Guinea baboon* ***Theropithecus gelada*** *gelada*

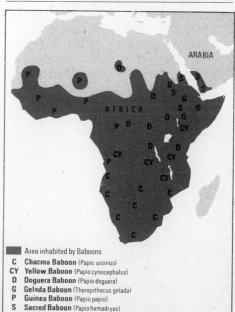

Area inhabited by Baboons

C   Chacma Baboon (Papio ursinus)
CY Yellow Baboon (Papio cynocephalus)
D   Doguera Baboon (Papio doguera)
G   Gelada Baboon (Theropithecus gelada)
P   Guinea Baboon (Papio papio)
S   Sacred Baboon (Papio hamadryas)

119

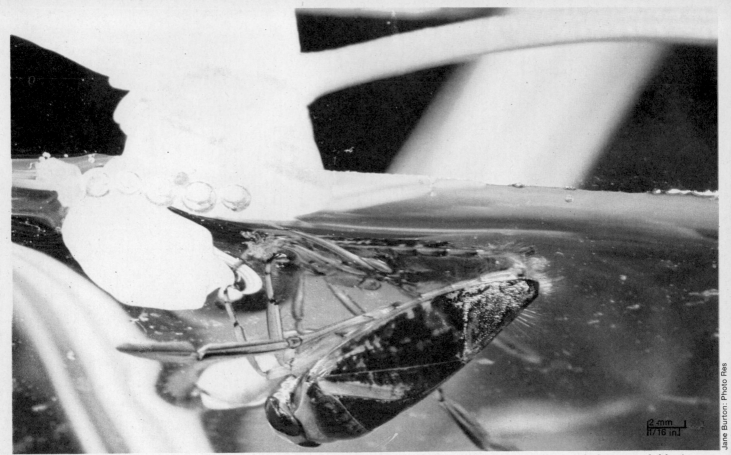

Backswimmer or water boatman hanging upside down from water surface by two pairs of legs and the tip of its abdomen which, surrounded by tiny hairs, is trapping a bubble of air for its next dive. The third pair of legs form the backswimmer's 'oars'. The yellow flower is a kingcup.

Backswimmer

A group of large-eyed aquatic bugs living in ponds, lakes and canals, including the backswimmers, boat-flies, water boatmen, or wherry-men, with a world-wide distribution. The commonest of the five British species is Notonecta glauca, *which can be seen in almost any stretch of sluggish water. It is rather more than ½ in. in length and of a pale brownish colour with darker thorax and undersides. Backswimmers are especially conspicuous for their long, paddle-like hind legs and their characteristic habit of resting upside down beneath the surface of the water.*

Aqualung diver

The colloquial name 'backswimmer' is particularly appropriate for this insect because it does actually swim upside down. Its very long hind legs—almost twice the length of the other two pairs—are fringed by a series of fine hairs, and with a few strokes of these oar-like legs the backswimmer can propel itself through the water at a remarkably fast rate. The hind legs are, in fact, used in unison, like oars, quite unlike the tripodal method of progression used by terrestrial insects. The wing-cases of the backswimmer join to form a ridge along the middle of the back, and when the insect is seen resting just beneath the surface with its long hind legs held out sideways the impression is of a keeled rowing boat with a pair of oars over the sides.

Backswimmers are extremely wary and at the slightest hint of danger will swim down from the top of the water. This needs great physical effort because the insect is very much lighter than water and would be continually and involuntarily rising to the surface, but for a powerful swimming action or a firm grip on some submerged object. This buoyancy is largely due to a bubble of air which the backswimmer always carries pressed to its abdomen by a series of bristles. Although fully aquatic, a backswimmer does not have gills and is unable to use the oxygen dissolved in the water. It must therefore get its air supply from outside, and this it does by rising periodically to the surface and sticking the tip of its abdomen out of the water. There is a channel formed by hairs on each side of the abdomen. These the insect opens at the surface, allowing air to flow in and then closes them again, trapping the air. These air-bubbles are therefore in direct contact with the backswimmer's spiracles or breathing holes which are arranged along the sides of the abdomen. The spiracles are protected by a further fringe of hairs which allows air in and keeps water out.

Although adapted to life in the water, and scarcely able to walk on land, backswimmers are strong fliers and can leave their natural element at any time; they are in consequence among the earliest colonisers of that fairly new feature, the water-filled gravel pit. During the Second World War emergency water tanks were set up everywhere, for use against fire from air-raids, and it was not uncommon to find backswimmers suddenly appearing in a tank, far from the nearest pond or river, surrounded by tall buildings. They would appear overnight, because they fly mostly at night, and are attracted to light, reflected from the water surface.

Voracious feeders

Backswimmers are extremely voracious feeders and it is always unwise to include them with other small forms of life in any aquarium. Mosquito and other fly larvae form a large part of their diet, but size alone does not always deter them. Large beetle larvae, tadpoles and even small fish are often attacked. The backswimmer's method of hunting is to hang motionless at the surface of the water, immediately swimming towards anything that catches its attention. It has excellent eyesight, but primarily it discovers its prey by a form of vibration-location: certain hairs on the hind legs can pick up the vibrations caused by small animals swimming nearby. Only when the backswimmer is within a few inches of its prey do the eyes play their part in securing its capture. Having captured its prey, the backswimmer then plunges its sharp rostrum (or beak) into the body of the victim, pumping in a toxic digestive fluid containing enzymes which rapidly break down the body tissues. The carcase is then held firmly by the prehensile fore-limbs while its internal tissues, now made fluid, are sucked out. The rostrum of the backswimmer can pierce human skin, and the toxic fluid pumped in may cause extremely painful symptoms. Fortunately, this only happens when the backswimmer is handled, and then only if handled carelessly, although the insect appears to be not over-particular what it attacks. In the days when cattle and horses drank far more commonly from village ponds, it was not unusual for backswimmers to attack their tender muzzles.

Life cycle

Mating in *Notonecta* usually occurs between about December in one year and late spring of the next. Batches of the elongated oval eggs are inserted into the stems of aquatic plants, such as Canadian pondweed, by the female's ovipositor. The eggs hatch after several weeks, the larvae, which are at first wingless, escaping by means of the hole originally made by the female's ovipositor. By late summer, these have become young adults and the older generation dies off. Only one generation is produced each year. Like all bugs, backswimmers undergo incomplete metamorphosis. That is, from the egg hatches a larva, which resembles the adult in form. Growth then proceeds by a series of moults.

Enemies

As a water insect, the backswimmer falls prey to the carnivorous animals present around its habitat. These include waterfowl, frogs, toads, and sometimes fish, such as trout or bass.

Seeing wrong way up

When we are standing or walking on firm ground we know we are the right way up partly because of our appreciation of the pull of gravity but also partly through our eyes. A passenger strapped in an aeroplane and unable to look out can be flying upside down and will be unaware of it. Anyone swimming underwater and caught in a strong turbulence can, if the water is murky, lose all sense of which way up he is.

A simple experiment that can be carried out on a backswimmer shows that their large compound eyes and well-developed sight play an important part in their orientation. Normally this insect rests just beneath the surface of the water, upside down. In a glass aquarium, with the top of the aquarium in darkness and a bright light shining from below the backswimmer will take up its position on the surface of the water with its lower surface directed down towards the light, so when we look at it from above it is in the position in which any other insect would be that was resting on the surface film. The backswimmer will try to live and swim in this position as long as light is maintained from below. This reaction to light is present in backswimmers even from a very early stage in their larval life.

Colin G Butler

△ *The young backswimmer is a nymph which gradually develops into an adult without the larva and pupa stages of higher insects.*

▽ *Adult backswimmer and young with mosquito pupae cleverly photographed from below to show their reflections in the surface.*

Jane Burton: Photo Res

class	**Insecta**
order	**Hemiptera**
suborder	**Heteroptera**
families	**Notonectidae, Pleidae**
genera	***Notonecta, Anisops, Plea***

Forestry, Fish & Game Commission, USA

Badger

The one European species of badger ranges right across Europe and Asia, from Ireland to China, yet it is one of the most elusive of mammals. It is nocturnal and generally so wary that it is rarely seen, even by many who set out with the intention of watching it.

The badger is a bear-like animal with a stocky 3ft body, short tail and short but powerful legs armed with strong claws on the front feet. It also walks on the soles of its feet like a bear, but the resemblance ends there. Both bear and badger are members of the Carnivora, or flesh-eaters, but they are in different families. The badger is placed in the family Mustelidae, along with the otter, stoat and weasel. A character of the mustelids is that their footprints show five toes. In this way the footprints of a badger can be distinguished from those of a dog, which show only four toes.

Another characteristic of mustelids is their musk or stink glands at the base of the tail. The best known owner of musk glands is the skunk, which can squirt a nauseating fluid at its enemies. Stoats and weasels use their musk to mark objects as a sign of ownership, but badgers do not use their glands for either of these purposes. They will, however, emit musk when excited, as when they are playing together, or when they are frightened.

At a distance, the badger's coat looks grey but the individual hairs are black and white. Most animals are lighter in colour on the underside of the body, but the badger has black on its belly and legs. The most striking part of the badger, however, is its head. This is white with two broad, black stripes running from behind the ears almost to the tip of the muzzle. The small eyes are placed in the black stripes and so are inconspicuous.

In China there is another animal resembling the badger. This is the hog badger which has very similar habits, but can easily be distinguished from the European badger by the naked pig-like snout, from which it got its name, and a much longer tail.

The American badger bears a greater resemblance to the European badger, but lacks the black and white striped head. It is widespread in North America from south-western Canada, south to central Mexico.

Nocturnal sett dwellers

The badger must have been well established in European folklore, as it has given its name, or local variants of it, to many towns and villages. For example, the old English name was brock, meaning particoloured, and there are in 'badger country' such places as Brockenhurst, Brockhampton, and Brocklesby, and in Germany, where the name for badger is 'dachs', we have such place names as Dachsbach, Dachsberg and Dachsfelden.

Badgers can be found throughout Britain, but are rarest in flat areas such as East Anglia. They often live surprisingly near to the centre of large cities and are found in practically all European and Asian countries, from just south of the Arctic Circle to the Mediterranean and the Himalayas. In the northern parts of their range they will hibernate, but in Britain they are active all winter.

Badgers are so rarely seen because of their nocturnal habits. Many supposedly nocturnal animals are often active during the day as well, but it is extremely rare for a badger to be seen about during daylight hours. Badgers emerge from their setts during the long, dark nights of autumn and winter, regularly one hour after sunset. The short nights of the summer months result in an earlier emergence.

If there is any disturbance, suspicious

◁ *American badger has a dark head with a white line on forehead and nape: It is known to US foresters as a silver tip after its fur. This usually inoffensive animal can put up a very tough fight as its defensive posture with hair on end and wicked-looking teeth imply.*

▷ *Badgers are known to follow the same well-trodden tracks on their nocturnal food-searching rambles. Because of this habit small gates can be built in wire fences, constructed to keep out rabbits and other pests from farm-lands and forests, but allowing the beneficial badgers to come and go as they wish.*

▽ *The fantastically strong claws on the front feet are used for digging the badger's home or sett.*

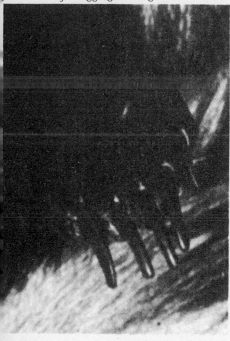

Forestry Commission London

sound or scent, the badger may remain underground for the night, and they will often fail to come out on bright moon-lit nights.

The setts, as badgerholes are called, are easily distinguished from the dwellings of foxes or rabbits by their large size and the mass of earth and stones that lies at the entrance. Confirmation that there are badgers in residence must, however, be made because foxes and rabbits will take up residence in them, sometimes when the badgers are still in occupation.

Signs of the badgers' presence are un-mistakable. It has regular, well-trodden paths leading from the sett which may be followed for some distance, often running to a stream or pond where the badgers habitually drink. Where they pass under barbed wire or brambles, wisps of distinct-ive black and white hairs can be found stuck in the barbs or thorns. Near the en-trance to the sett there are more definite signs of activity. Scratching posts indicate where a badger has stood on its hind legs and scratched the trunk of a tree with its forepaws. Around the mouth of the hole and along the paths leading to it fresh vegetation will be strewn—bracken, blue-bells and other plants that have been col-ected for bedding. The badger gathers these in its fore legs and shuffles back-wards leaving a trail of plants.

Badgers have a reputation for being especially clean animals, largely because they frequently change their bedding and also dig latrines, shallow pits that can be found within 20 yd or so of the sett.

The favourite sites for setts, which may be vast underground systems with many entrances, are in woodland, preferably those bordered by pastures. Sandy soil seems to be preferred.

Cubs born underground

The male, or boar, and the female, or sow, badgers probably pair for life. Mating takes place in July or August but the embryos do not begin to develop until December or January. This is another example of de-layed implantation. That is, the fertilised egg undergoes its first few divisions, after which growth is arrested for some time. (See also under armadillo on p. 83.) The young, one to five in number, are born during February or March. At birth they measure no more than 5 in., of which 1½ in. is tail.

For the first 6–8 weeks of their life they stay underground, then make their first, tentative visits to the outside world. The routine for leaving the sett is that the sow appears first, sniffing the air and be-having even more cautiously than usual. Then she turns back to the entrance and coaxes her cubs to come out behind her.

At first they stay out for only a very short time, scampering back to safety at the slightest alarm. After a week or so they be-come bolder and start exploring the neigh-bourhood and playing rough and tumble games. Later they are taken out to learn to feed themselves and they eventually leave their parents in October.

Main food is earthworms

Badgers belong to the Carnivora or flesh-eaters, and an examination of a badger's skull suggests an animal equipped for attacking and consuming large prey. The teeth are strong and there are long ridges around the hinges of the jaws that prevent them from being dislocated. Yet the badger lives on a wide variety of soft food. Earth-worms are a major item, as were young rabbits before the epidemic rabbit disease, myxomatosis, made them rare. Mice, voles, moles, frogs, snails, beetles and even hedgehogs and wasps make up the animal content of the diet, while windfall apples, bulbs, acorns, blackberries and grass are also eaten. Fungi are sampled, and cereal crops suffer when badgers flatten large areas to get the ears. Poultry killing occurs occasionally but is not typical; the majority never touch them. The reason is usually scarcity of normal food or a single animal that has acquired the habit. Badgers have sometimes been found in hen houses, with

△ *Two young badgers at the mouth of their sett. This is a series of tunnels which may be quite deep and very ancient.*

▽ *Badger caught by photographer changing bedding. When bringing in bedding it shuffles backwards without looking where it is going.*

none of the inhabitants disturbed. The American badger can burrow rapidly, digging out the rabbits and rodents on which it feeds.

The proportions of the different items taken varies with season and weather. On wet nights, for instance, badgers will go to pastureland to feed on earthworms, and suckling sows normally eat little else but earthworms.

Enemies

Badgers have little to fear, except from man, who in past times has trapped them to provide sport by badger-baiting with dogs, or, at all times, because they have killed his poultry. Today they probably suffer most in Britain from rabbit clearance societies, who regularly gas rabbit warrens. Although gassing badgers is illegal, rabbits in a sett are sufficient excuse.

Recognition marks

It is often said that the grey body and the conspicuous black and white stripes on the head serve as camouflage, simulating shafts of moonlight coming through the trees. Yet badgers avoid moonlight and when they do show themselves they are surprisingly conspicuous. White objects will stand out if there is any light at all.

Another theory is that the stripes are a warning coloration, a warning to other animals to keep away from the badger's bite. Certainly there is a tendency for animals with a powerful form of defence to have a striking colour pattern. For example, the skunk, with its powerfully deterrent odour, has a conspicuous band of white along the head and back and a bushy white tail. Similarly, bees and wasps have warning colours of black and yellow. Predatory animals learn to associate these with an unpleasant experience, and so leave well alone.

There is a drawback to this idea with badgers. Against whom is this warning to operate? It is difficult to find a serious enemy of the badger even by examining the animals that lived in Europe a thousand years ago. Bears normally do not prey on animals of this sort, wolves are mainly active by day and lions go for a different type of prey. A further difficulty is that other badgers, the American badger and the hog badger, for instance, do not have these facial markings, yet survive. The probability is that the white markings help badgers to recognise each other in the dark.

The badger's reaction to danger is quite spectacular. If startled, it emits a violent snorting, enough in itself to scare anything not expecting it. Then it literally bristles the hair of the body standing on end so that it looks twice the normal size. Anyone who suddenly met a badger when it has 'blown up' will know the shock-value it has.

class	**Mammalia**
order	**Carnivora**
family	**Mustelidae**
genera & species	***Meles meles*** European badger ***Arctonyx collaris*** hog badger ***Taxidea taxus*** American badger